THREE WRITERS | ONE PHOTOGRAPHER

Garrett M. Brown

Barbara Crane

Bill Davis

Marie Pal-Brown

Three **Writers** | One **Photographer**

An Anthology

LAGOON
HOUSE
PRESS

Three Writers / One Photographer
Garrett M. Brown, Barbara Crane, Bill Davis, Marie Pal-Brown

"There Had to Be a Rothko," by Barbara Crane,
    first published in *Open: Journal of Arts & Letters,* December 2019.
"The Raft of the Medusa," by Barbara Crane,
    first published in *Birmingham Arts Journal,* Volume 7, Issue 3.
"The Beating of Wings," by Barbara Crane,
    first published in *Hevria,* March 2019.
"Enclose my Heart, this Blessed Wonder," by Marie Pal-Brown,
    first published in *Valyermo Chronicle,* Number 269, Summer 2022.
"Advent, Colorado Lagoon," by Marie Pal-Brown,
    first published under the title "Broken Alleluia" in *Valyermo Chronicle,*
    Number 269, Summer 2022.
"Riot Act," by Garrett M. Brown, debuted at *EST-LA,* Winterfest 2019.
"The Tragedy of Modern Man in Three Acts... by Garry Brown"
    and "My New Yorker Cover," by Garrett M. Brown,
    debuted on Zoom, *EST-LA,* Winterfest 2020.

ISBN 978-0-9972609-7-7
Library of Congress Registration number: TXU 2-358-134
Cover and book design by Ellison / Goodreau
Cover image and photograph "Woman Viewing a Rothko" by Bill Davis
Pen-and-ink drawings by Garrett M. Brown
Sketch accompanying "The Raft of Medusa" by Kai Goldfein

Printed in the United States
Lagoon House Press
Long Beach, CA
www.lagoonhousepress.com

For Holly Prado Northup
Poet and Writer
1938–2019

Beloved teacher, mentor, friend

Contents

Foreword

Lagoon House Press came into being in 2015. It was inspired by Cahuenga Press in Los Angeles. One of the members of Cahuenga Press, the late Holly Prado, taught writing workshops out of her home in East Hollywood for over 40 years. The members of Lagoon House Press—Barbara Crane, Marie Pal-Brown, Garrett M. Brown and Bill Davis—as well as myself—were part of Holly's workshops at one time or another. The two presses have a deep connection—they are sibling presses and Holly is our creative mother.

The friends who formed Lagoon House Press share interests in literature, art, film and theater. They did so in order to have control over all aspects of the publication of the work, and to support each other's mutual creative endeavors. *Three Writers / One Photographer* is LHP's fourth publication, along with *When Water Was Everywhere* by Barbara Crane in 2016, followed by *Daughter of the Enemy* by Marie Pal-Brown, and *The Second Mrs. Price* by Toni Fuhrman.

Three Writers / One Photographer is a feast of memories and of the imagination. It spreads itself out to us in course after course and nourishes our spirits with its fullness of life and solid imagery.

In her introduction to her group of stories, Barbara Crane discusses the great joy writing brings to her. She writes novels, including her brilliant book *When Water Was Everywhere.* Between novels, short stories emerge, three of which are included in this collection.

The first story, "There Had to Be a Rothko," charts the response of a woman recently retired, a woman who has only her "impeccable taste" to sustain her. When she stands in front of a Rothko painting, she sobs. Anyone who has been in the Rothko Chapel in Houston can relate. It is a deeply moving experience. Our narrator goes back again to see the paintings and is again profoundly affected. She decides that she must spend the night with the Rothkos. Much of the rest of the story describes her planning for this. We leave her stretched out on the floor in the center of the Rothko room, becoming one with the paintings.

This marvelous story describes our relationship with art, how it can enter into and transform us. It is both an extended metaphor and a true description of what can happen in the presence of extraordinary art. The story is accompanied by a wonderful photo by Bill Davis of a woman standing mesmerized in front of a Rothko painting.

The second story, "The Raft of the Medusa," involves a family at a diving camp owned by Bedouins at the tip of the Sinai Peninsula, and a narrator who invents their story. "Here was this family demanding that I write about them..." It is a fascinating tale of the interplay between life and the world of the imagination. We never know what actually happens to the Dutch family. We only know the narrator's version.

The last story, "The Beating of Wings" is an account of the plagues of Moses in ancient Egypt as told by the wife of a worker whose job is to keep the slaves working on the pyramid. We wait in horror as the "beating wings" of the last plague sweep over their house, not protected by the blood of a lamb, a powerful and terrifying tale that takes us back to Biblical times.

The three stories skillfully navigate the relationship between life and our imagination of it. The two are intertwined until they become one, a spiritual merging, like the woman and the Rothko painting.

Next is a feast of poems by Marie Pal-Brown. Marie thinks of poems as "invited guests." Like dreams, they become "visible in the imagery and musings that come upon us during our waking reality." The real and the numinous merge in her work. The poems are in several sections, the first of which concerns Marie's garden in Venice, a particularly moving selection. Hers is a garden filled with plants that are remembrances of the dead: succulents for her father, stargazer lilies for the son of a friend, and most poignant, the magnolia tree planted the week her mother died. The spirit of Marie's mother permeates the garden, which Marie worked on as her mother stepped back from tending her own garden along the Rhine. These poems are prayers to the spirits gone before and "to a god forever imagined/said over and over..."

Her garden is a sacred space and into it comes her lover,

eventually her husband, Garrett M. Brown, whom she met in Holly Prado's workshop. These tender, powerful love poems are a testament to her commitment to being in the world fully, and to art, both hers and her husband's.

When Marie moved from Venice to the lagoon house in Long Beach with her husband, it took some time for the spirit of the lagoon to open to her, but gradually it did: her mother's spirit is present in the green-breasted hummingbird that hovers at her window each morning; she watches a challenged boy and his father walk along the water—and sees the wonder in this. Then in December, during Advent, the sky over the lagoon opens up as she watches the Christmas lights doubled in the water's reflection—"I wait for the angels to raise their trumpets."

In the Abbey poems, the presence of spirit becomes more specific when reality is "made holy/ by light from an ordinary lamp." She watches sunlight stream through stained glass windows. She weeps for the chopped down trees as a monk prays for them. She contemplates the endurance of prayer, of works of art: "The luminous ones, their words/endure through time and space... nothing fades into nothingness." Her language is clear and down to earth,

and is filled with a luminosity of spirit. The world has become a "feast of all that is, that was, that will be," and it is our feast.

As Garrett M. Brown ("2 r's, 2 t's") says in his introduction to the next course of our feast, his stories speak of his own immersion and love of the creative process. Garrett is multi-talented—he is an accomplished and hard-working actor who came to the arts as a painter. I have been fortunate to enjoy his bright and lovely work at his home and studio in Long Beach.

As we see in these selections, he is also a gifted writer. The first two stories are what Garrett calls hybrid-memories, memories with some fictional elements. They are poignant, warm and funny, full of life that took me back to my own early days on the East coast. "The Tragedy of Man in Three Acts" recounts Garrett's relationship with a difficult AP English teacher his senior year in high school in Darien, Connecticut, a teacher who ridiculed him (Garrett was an athlete, a "jock") until he turned in a play instead of an essay on the tragedy of man. His teacher loved it, and respected him from then on. The story has a coda: six years after graduation, Garrett was writing poems and located his old teacher to show them to him. His teacher opened the door, a completely changed man out of the classroom, who remembered Garrett and his play. He took the poems without asking Garrett in—no small talk, and a week later, Garrett returned.

"Keep writing, Brown. Keep reading, lots of reading, and keep writing." That was it—encouragement in his cold, distant way—who *is* this man, we wonder. But he had a profound effect on Garrett, who kept reading and kept writing.

The next story is a delightful tale of almost getting a *New Yorker* cover—well, at least getting inside the magazine's offices—which has a marvelous ending. These two stories have a light, loving touch. They are a delight to read.

The tone changes in the last story which is a fiction piece, not a memoir. It is heartbreaking, brutal and beautifully written, all told in the voice of Riot, an injured football player waiting for help in the locker room. The story helped me understand two things about football: first, the deep addictive physicality of it, which in this story has a spiritual component for Riot, "... His whole body, demeanor could shift, transform. 'An extra gear,' some said... He is an unbridled muscular fluency." I begin to understand the love of this game, even in its brutality.

The story becomes a tragedy and the second thing that becomes clear at the end of it is the terrible toll the game takes on the body and mind. We leave Riot in the hospital, screaming and sobbing.

Thank you, Garrett, for giving us a deep and powerful understanding of this ferocious game.

Included in this splendid collection are the photographs of Bill Davis. His photos are not staged. He takes photos as he goes, carrying his heavy camera wherever he travels—India, Thailand, Mexico, the Galapagos among others. He photographs "anything that moves."

His bird photos are spirited and humorous, especially the Blue Footed Booby, the stunning line of cormorants and, of course, the delightful penguins. They are wide ranging and fun—ending with an iguana staring right at us. Bill's favorite photo is of the gray whale calf, which captures its enormous eye in the water. It is an extraordinary photo where we seem to look deep into the heart of the wild.

In addition to the creatures, there are photos of statues and architecture taken during his travels, and a poignant one of a farmer plowing a curved line around a hillside. Like so much in this superb book, it is exquisite and full of spirit.

This collection is a feast that

nourishes the soul. We are fed in so many ways: by the beauty of nature, the revelations of art, the memories of our youth, the joy of the imagination, and the depth of our responses to our world.
I am grateful to Barbara Crane, Marie Pal-Brown, Garrett M. Brown and Bill Davis for sharing their wonderful banquet with us.

Phoebe MacAdams Ozuna
August, 2022

Three Stories | Barbara Crane

Always Working

Writing is one of my great joys in life. To hunt for what I want to say. To find the right words to say it.

I didn't know that joy until I was in my mid-thirties, when I was released from a prolonged writer's block by the chance statement, long since forgotten, of USC Professor of Linguistics and Rhetoric, Dr. Ross Winterowd. That quirky, brilliant man set me off on a path that has been frustrating at times, yet always rewarding. I keep at it, whatever I am working on—and I am always working on something.

Most often, I write novels. At this time, in 2023, I have published two novels and am working on a third. It took me ten years to write the first novel and ten years to write the second. I'm in the third year of working on my current novel, wondering if it will take me seven more to finish.

Between novels, ideas for short stories surface. Each of my three short stories in this book were inspired by a unique circumstance.

I have always loved the work of Mark Rothko, the 20th century abstract expressionist painter. The story, "There Had to Be a Rothko," was prompted by an experience I, myself, longed to put into play, as I stood transfixed in a room of Rothko canvases at the Museum of Contemporary Art in Los Angeles.

"The Raft of the Medusa" came from a stay in a Bedouin diving camp at the tip of the Sinai Peninsula in 1998. I was there with friends, celebrating Passover in the desert. It was a magical moment, and I made magic with it, that is, I imagined something that wasn't there and convinced myself that it was.

In my seventieth year, I discovered a bond with my Jewish faith that had always eluded me. My third story, "The Beating of Wings" came from my evolving interest in the Torah, the first five books of the Hebrew Bible. As I wrote this story, I thought I was being heretical, but I soon learned that, in Judaism, every line of inquiry is valid. To my added surprise, *Hevria,* a magazine published by and for the Modern Orthodox movement—with a more observant audience than that of my own Reform community—was happy to accept it.

There Had to Be a Rothko

Ruth sobbed the first time she stood in front of a Mark Rothko painting. In the middle of the art museum, in the center of the room, her head bowed to her chest, her hands covering her face. If the guards looked at her that quiet January afternoon as they strolled through the galleries, she wasn't aware.

When her sobs had quieted to low gasps, she peered through her fingers to her shoes. Both navy blue, but not a pair. Her embarrassment at wearing unmatched shoes prompted her to flee the museum. She found her car in the parking garage and hurried home.

For some weeks, Ruth avoided the museum. Retirement had left her with little money to spend. She had not accumulated family, friends, or interests in her working years. Even the detritus of her career, well-placed on the fireplace mantel and on tables next to the sofa, held no meaning for her.

The only thing left to her was her impeccable taste.

She never understood how she had acquired that taste from her very average, working-class parents. But she had traded on it in every job, beginning with her first as assistant buyer for designer fashion at Saks Fifth Avenue and ending as home furnishings buyer at Macy's, forty-five years later.

Along the way had been Robinson's and Saks Fifth Avenue in Southern California. Then two heady years at Bonwit Teller in New York, another at Bloomingdale's and then, back to California. Macy's in the Beverly Center was her last job. If the choice had been hers, she would have worked again in fashion at Bloomingdale's or chosen shoes for Nieman Marcus. But it wasn't.

On Ruth's 65th birthday, the young human resources representative at Macy's gave her a month's severance and retained her practiced smile until Ruth left the office. No explanation given; Ruth didn't ask.

Ruth missed the feel of fabric under her fingertips. The *peau de soie* when she began her career, the Indian silk of later years, the Balenciaga sweep of skirt, the complex hues of a bargello-stitched upholstered chair. Fabric was a sensual experience. She loved those brushes with elegance, temporary as they were.

A month passed until she approached the museum again. This time she wore black pumps with sensible heels and not-sensible, very pointed toes.

These were her memories as she stood in the museum's room of Rothko canvases a second time: The lapis lazuli-colored ceramic cup—a gift from her aunt on her eleventh birthday. Her father's face, a pasty yellow, as he lay on the hospital gurney, the last time she saw him. The shocking pink sundress she wore, backless and braless, to meet her Italian lover at the foot of Rome's Spanish Steps. A porcelain bowl, its gleam of polished ebony, so small, so expensive, that she should have bought on her first trip to Japan.

Ruth waited until a group of high school students left the gallery before she again stood facing the Rothko canvas that had moved her to tears. A large black rectangle shaded into a blue that was nearly black. Above the black rectangle, another, lighter blue, narrower than the one beneath. Above the blue, a larger one again, a blue-veined rust. All colors melted into their inky surround.

Transfixed, she pondered questions she had rarely considered. What did it mean to be alive? What was it all for? She had dedicated her life to making women and their surroundings beautiful, giving no thought to what would come after.

Ruth began to cry as she had the first time. Tears rolled down her cheeks. The tears became sobs, the sobs deepened. A thought interrupted her tears. She must spend a night alone with these paintings.

She dismissed the idea. Impossible. The museum was guarded by day and certainly by night. There were cameras everywhere. She could see one in the ceiling corner now. She wasn't a thief who knew how to disable cameras or locks. She would be caught and end up in jail.

Ruth made her way slowly through the museum's galleries, finding many canvases to admire. No artist moved her the way Rothko did. Finally, she left.

Again, weeks passed. She attended a book group at the local library and took long walks in her neighborhood. She shopped for groceries, careful to spend only the money she had allotted for food. She leafed through magazines collected when she was earning a salary.

Through every one of her days, and as she tossed and turned at night, ran a persistent thought, "I want to spend one night with the Rothkos," accompanied by a frisson of excitement. She vacuumed, swept her small kitchen, dusted the tables she had owned for years until the refrain changed, "I *will* spend one night with the Rothkos."

By the end of February, Ruth had a plan. She began to ferret out certain clothes in thrift stores: plain colors, nondescript, hats with wide brims that concealed part of her face. She rescued old, worn shoes from her building's trash bins. Nothing like the clothes she usually wore, nothing that had any style. Wearing this cast-off apparel, she visited the museum several times late in the day when the galleries would be likely to have emptied out. The few guards that patrolled the rooms ignored her.

Once, she remained in the women's bathroom until nearly closing time. She hurried out of the building as the public address system intoned, "The museum is now closing." She was pleased. No one had checked to see if anyone remained in the bathroom stalls.

Time passed more quickly during these winter days as she thought and re-thought her strategy, focusing on one piece after another. Sometimes, engrossed in a detail, she forgot to leave her apartment even to take a walk or shop for food.

There were times also when fear overpowered her. At those moments, Ruth lay on her couch covered by the worn comforter that had been hers as a child. She shook with terror at being discovered in the museum. Even more frightening was what awaited her if she succeeded, if she found herself in the Rothko room, alone, in the dark.

The day of the spring equinox, Ruth entered the museum at four o'clock on a Wednesday afternoon. The museum would close at five, as usual. She would have until eight-thirty the next morning when the first administrative staff arrived. She had carefully confirmed all these details.

Only one guard would be on duty all night. She had seen the monitor where he watched the galleries' cameras. They were located at the reception desk: a dozen small monitors, one for each room and the parking garage. None in the bathrooms, none in the halls. The Rothko room's camera surveyed the floor and ceiling. But she had noticed a far corner of the gallery where the camera's eye did not reach.

Ruth brushed aside the wide brim of her hat to take in the Rothkos in the lighted gallery. Eight canvases filled the space, floor to ceiling. To the left of the one that had been her first favorite was a red rectangle above a larger blue one, like her favorite, surrounded by a narrow black border. Another: two black rectangles divided by a red line. Although she no longer dissolved into tears as she had on her first visits, she felt the power of the paintings. She felt moved as she never had in a church, even in the most famous cathedrals in Europe. What she felt exactly, she couldn't find the words to describe. She knew that after this night with Rothko, she would.

At four forty-five, when the public address system announced, "The museum will be closing in fifteen minutes," Ruth walked leisurely to the first-floor women's bathroom. She pushed open the door and entered a stall near the back wall. Instead of pulling down her slacks, she sat down on the toilet seat and brought her knees to her chest. She balanced precariously until, as she had expected, a guard knocked at the door. He pushed it open and called, "Anyone here? We're closing in ten minutes." Hearing no response, he left.

Ruth breathed again. She lowered her legs to the floor. She had completed the first step. The lights went off, plunging her into darkness. She drew a small flashlight from her pocket, switched it on. Now she only needed to wait.

Ruth had planned to emerge from the bathroom at nine o'clock, but time dragged too slowly. The anxiety she had carried through all her weeks of planning gave way to exhaustion. After barely two hours had passed, afraid that she would fall asleep and not wake until the morning, she gave in. Leaving the bathroom, she moved quickly down the hall and stopped. The next move would be the most difficult.

Holding the flashlight securely, she took a deep breath and dropped to the floor without making a sound. She lay there until her breath resumed its normal pattern. When she was ready, she rose to her hands and knees and began to crawl slowly forward toward the Rothko gallery. Situated as it was in the first room next to the entrance foyer, she didn't have far to go. She stayed close to the wall, hoping that the camera would not pick up her form or, worse, that the lone guard patrolling the museum would not choose this moment to appear out of the dark.

Slowly she crawled along the floor, placing one arm and one leg firmly, then shifting her weight to the other side. When she had made it across the foyer and into the Rothko room, she shrank back against the wall. She pressed her knees to her chest. She wanted to laugh out loud. If anyone had seen her, a 66-year-old woman wearing baggy pants and a mustard-colored jacket, they wouldn't recognize her as the smartly dressed woman who had headed the fashion departments of major retail stores.

She heard footsteps. The guard passed nearby; his flashlight beam moved from side to side but did not alight on her. She held her breath until she heard his steps in the next room.

Ruth sat against the wall until her eyes became accustomed to the dark. Despite her plan to stay there all night, she began to creep toward the center of the gallery. She moved by instinct, by desire. There was only one place for her in the world, and that was in the center of the room. Where she could feel the force of all the Rothkos at once. Where she could feel.

She moved forward slowly until she reached the spot she judged to be the room's center. Once there, she lay back on the floor. She let the canvases enter her body: the heat of Rothko's red through her heart, the warmth of blue through the soles of her feet, the tingle of yellow, the orange, the green. Her body throbbed with color until, slowly, the throbbing diminished, leaving her with a sensation she could only describe as peace.

Like Rothko's rectangles, she was immersed in the dark, grounded but not static. Infinite in depth. Infinite in life and what lay beyond.

She did not turn on her flashlight or raise her arm to peer at the luminous hands of her watch. She lay still. Content. Unafraid.

Time passed. Minutes. Hours.

She waited while the Rothkos filled her body. She waited until they became her beating heart. Because that was what it was about, wasn't it? You couldn't see through to the other side. If there was life in the darkness, you had to trust it was there.

The Raft of the Medusa

I met a young Dutch boy in the Sinai, at a diving camp owned by Bedouins. The sun already scorched the common area that opened out from eight palm-thatched rooms. They weren't much, these rooms. The size of a closet, enough for a mattress on a concrete slab and a small table. They were perfect—only enough space to change from bathing suit to shorts, to sleep the few hours possible after all had been said at dinner, and the sun belonged to someplace else on earth.

The young boy's room was next to mine. I saw him looking at me, and I said hello. He spoke perfect American English. I thought he was an American, but he wasn't. He was Dutch, he said. His father was a businessman. He and his family-mother, father, sister-lived in Cairo. I looked over at them. His father and mother were stepping outside their door into the semi-circle filled by tables and chairs outside our rooms. His father was lean and sturdy with large shoulders, his mother delicate and strong. A dancer, I thought. His parents wore the same look we all did in the morning. Tousled hair, squinting into the sun, only half-believing that light could be that bright. There was nothing to prepare you for a sea quite so blue, quite so close.

The boy's manner was compelling; I soon focused on him again. But not before I saw the girl who had tucked herself into a dark corner. I took it that this was his sister; no one else would have been standing there. Then I recalled seeing her the night before. She had been sitting with her brother on a low wall outside the dining area, holding the same blanket she was now, a lifeless gray thing, although it may have been a brighter color when new. She clutched it to her face and sucked the thumb that held the blanket close to her.

"My mother rides horses across the Nile Valley," the boy volunteered, not realizing that to me, a writer, that simple sentence would make my head spin. Rides horses. I wanted to find out what kind of horse she rode. What did she see as she rode? Who rode with her, and what did she wear? Why did she ride? She was beautiful. How many men were in her life? And why did she need them?

And what was the quality of love she gave her husband?

I wanted to know them. And because I couldn't-there wasn't time, they certainly didn't appear to want conversation-I made them up. I'd rather have known the true answers, but I took what I could. After all, who is to say we can know our own stories, each unique and complex, more clearly than can a stranger?

That's how it began. I was an American tourist at a diving camp in the Sinai with good friends I hadn't seen in ten years. I met Stefan, the Dutch boy who spoke English. I exchanged nods with his parents, Bart and Els. I considered trying to draw out Louki, the girl, but the wall she had built around herself was too formidable. Undoubtedly, they thought, if they noticed me at all, that I was occupied with my own friends. I must have looked that way as I set the roughhewn table for breakfast and drank coffee brewed in a propane demijohn. But the whole time I was watching them. I saw Els comb Louki's long blonde hair, pulling the comb carefully through the strands that resembled the faded remnants of her blanket. I watched for words they exchanged between each other, in Dutch, in English, but they said very little. I gave up watching and went down to the water where I gathered my courage and swam out over the coral.

When I returned, my skin beaded with cool water, I saw them a distance away. They sat on their blanket as if clinging to a raft, four survivors looking out to the Red Sea. What was each thinking? After all, we were too far away to see Saudi Arabia. There was nothing to look at except Tiran Island. In the morning, no tour boats approached the small island and the few sea bathers weren't much to look at—clumps of tourists quietly paddling in the shallow water, not even a child who called out loudly; the seascape was as starkly barren as the land. At times like these, we are engaged in our private thoughts or in deliberately not thinking.

Bart: *Quiet. Good. I love these people, my children, my wife, can't speak, cry, not here, wife, ankle, calf, thigh, stomach, nipple, need.*

Stefan: *One good fish, I want to see just one good fish, a flounder, a barracuda, big one, liked Tiran Island, only us, Dad's big, let's go swimming Dad, let's go now.*

Els: *Hot sun, want cool water, Bart never talks, what is he thinking? Shall we go now? Monday work, see Josef maybe, stop picking at your blanket Louki, please stop picking, oh Louki, I worry about you.*

Louki: *Help me, help me, help me, help me, mommy, daddy, Stefan, please.*

I saw the four of them on their blanket in the hot sun, their silence. Perhaps they felt so comfortable with each other, they didn't need to speak. Perhaps it was so hot, they couldn't. But I saw tension in their bodies, how Louki bent over her blanket, how Bart paced the square of blue cotton. It almost seemed as if they were bending into the wind. Only Stefan moved unselfconsciously; his face displayed calm interest.

Louki is only seven, after all, how much does she need? Mothers are important at that age. More important than fathers, Bart told himself. He never saw his own father pay any particular attention to his sisters. Yes, fathers should stay out of the picture, he was sure of that. What could he do anyhow? He couldn't take her to the bathroom, he couldn't tell her about menstruation, he couldn't tell her about boys. He didn't even know about boys himself, hardly remembered being one.

His life began when he met Els. Had he ever been a boy like Stefan? A boy without worries? *Too much to think about. Not important. Think about work. Don't think about Els.* That's how he lived. Between a yes and a no.

It was still early when they returned to their rooms to gather swim fins, snorkels and masks. I moved closer to Stefan and asked where they were going.

"A little farther along the beach. The reef drops into deep water."

"Deeper than here?"

"Much. You can't see the ocean bottom at all. You're swimming and looking at fish and clams and coral. Very close to you. Then, you're on top of nothing, nothing at all. You can't see the bottom. Nothing."

I almost shivered with fear. I knew that he was as taken by the implicit danger as I. More than anything, I wanted to keep him talking. His hair was tan and prickly short, an exact replica of his father's. His body would resemble his father's one day also. I could already see the broad shoulders of a medium tall man. But where his father avoided looking at anyone outside his family, Stefan's blue green eyes searched my face. He was ten. I was fifty. I knew if I told him a secret he would never tell.

Louki stood nearby sucking her blanket-entwined fingers. Bart emerged from the room carrying a canvas bag, Els behind him. Els was gorgeous, I realized then. She wasn't glamorous in the way we Americans see movie stars, with their ambition-hardened stomachs and jaws. Her body was more sinuous, hard in muscle, yes, but rounded as coral coils. Curve of her calf, curve of her butt, curve of her upper arm. A person could write a poem about each one. Her husband had.

Oh, how he wanted to know his wife loved him (the children never doubted their mother's love). Often, all he could think about was Els. Last Monday morning, in a meeting. Leo's office. He saw his hand tremble as he reached for his coffee; he quickly clutched his cup. *Had anyone noticed? The cup, its handle, the curve, his wife's ass. How could anyone feel this way about his own wife ten years after marriage? What if someone saw me tremble? Ten years ago, I caught a cold, I'd say. A cold? Leo would raise his eyebrows. Ten years ago?*

His disease was advancing. He desired her more than when he met her. Ten years. They had made love four thousand times. Ten thousand times he had wanted her. If he had been ill for so long, he'd be unable to work. Desire was asymptomatic. He might remain for years in this condition without anyone suspecting.

The family was ready to leave. I turned my attention to the beach again where sunbathers were already grabbing the small patches of shade created by a few stunted palm trees. I thought about Els, her life, her loves.

"Josef, I'm going now. I have to get home and pack for the Sinai."

"Hmm?" Josef opened one eye and appraised Els who was fastening her skirt and pulling on her sandals in one quick movement. She raked her fingers through her red-brown hair and approached the bed.

"One more kiss," he teased.

"No," she glanced at the window high above the bed. The slow blue of twilight. Was it more than an hour ago she had heard the muezzin call for prayer? "Bart will be home soon. I was crazy to do this today."

"Not crazy. Delicious, warm, exciting. Maybe a little crazy, in a good way." His eyes crinkled at the corners.

"I can't get caught in your word games now, Josef." She opened the door. "I'll call you next week." She was using her blonde voice. The color of British women. Quiet authority. Self-confident. Different than an hour ago. *yes, Josef, now, yes, the red-brown voice, round as her butt, muscle and warm.*

Els left without looking back. Sinew and mane whirled out the door. She plunged into the street outside Josef's apartment building, competing for space on the narrow sidewalks with spindly-legged young boys racing home before dark, the faithful returning from prayer, old women dragging sacks of vegetables, and Arabs wearing traditional galabeya striding toward coffee houses. She wove through them, her mind racing faster than her feet. *No, Josef, can't stay with you, don't want to stay with you, home, Stefan, Louki. Bart.* After his name never any punctuation but a period. Louki was another matter. Louki stood alone, but different than Bart. *Why, why, why are you so sad, my beauty, my Louki?*

The beach grew even quieter towards noon. The sun scorched the sand. Later a mild breeze would be our relief; now, nothing stirred. Still, I had no thought of going anywhere else. I didn't want to retreat to an air-conditioned dining room even if I had known where one was. The hours between noon and four dragged the first day. After that, an hour became like ten minutes. Before I knew it, we were talking about dinner.

 Yesterday I was content; today, restless. Here was this family demanding that I write about them. I had to admit it was too hot to write, but I scribbled notes every time I felt overwhelmed with my imaginings, then put down my journal again. I gazed at the sea. Like Els and Louki, I was looking for something I couldn't name.

An Egyptian secretary of state, an American businessman named Charles, a British Egyptologist. Josef, a physician, was the lover closest to her world, a Dutch nurse in a Cairo hospital like Els. She was drawn to the government minister's conversation, the American's bold neckties, the Brit's ass. She didn't need these men but she took them nevertheless. Josef was another matter. Only he had seen her as the cool, dispassionate nurse, touching pillows and foreheads.

 She had to be a mother. She didn't have to be a wife. She didn't want to do heroic, hard things. It was easier to be a mother if she were a wife. She didn't have affairs because she wanted to drive her husband crazy. She didn't want him crazy over her. She had affairs because she fell in love and when you fall in love, you make love. She didn't stay in love for long. She had too much else to do.

 Els ran home, her body a tuning fork to Josef's hands, her thoughts as tangled as her life.

 Louki waited. She sat on her bed, holding her blanket tight against her chest. *Daddy will come home soon. Maybe Daddy will sit here with me and ask me about school. I'll tell him, "Daddy, I rode a horse at school today. A horse. Just like Mommy." He'd like that because he loves Mommy. If I were as pretty as Mommy, he'd love me too.*

That morning, Louki had passed their bedroom. Els was in the shower; Louki heard the water running. Bart was wearing slacks and a white cotton undershirt. In his palm, he held the small diamond earrings his wife wore every day, studying them. He had a funny look on his face, half mad, half sad. Louki wanted to tell her Daddy a story that would make him laugh. Stefan came up behind her and said, "Boo!" She jumped. Daddy came out and said in his angry voice, "Louki, Stefan, stop playing around. Go in and let Fatima give you breakfast." He shut the bedroom door. Louki stared at the closed door until Stefan touched her shoulder. Head bowed over her blanket, she followed him down the hall.

That day my friends and I skipped a formal lunch. We had shopped in Haifa's outdoor market the day before we left, buying kilos of kibbutz-grown tomatoes, dates from Dead Sea orchards, Turkey's golden apricots, four varieties of olives. These and the more mundane carrots, celery and hard-boiled eggs were more than we needed. Five or six times a day we walked up the sand to buy cold bottled water. Those first mouthfuls of icy water held more pleasure than a four-star meal.

The resort drew Egyptians, Israelis but also Finns and Czechs, Italians, French. When I sat on the sand or in the open-air dining room, I understood how the Middle East came to be known as the crossroads of the world. I mused about this firsthand knowledge my journey had given me.

Sometimes I let myself think about the marriage I had left behind. Begun in sunlight, ending in shadow. Like Géricault's painting, "The Raft of the Medusa," a long-distance voyage that was ending only after the strong had devoured the weak, and the survivors were left clinging to one another, praying to be saved.

"I'm home," Els announced as she opened the door. Louki and Stefan ran down the hall and threw their arms around her. Els felt overwhelmed by guilt. Why had she spent the afternoon with Josef when she loved her children so? Bart opened the door behind her. She turned toward him and saw he wore the look of a man who was suffering an intense headache and overwhelming relief at the same time. "Is anything wrong?" she asked.

Bart scowled. "No," he answered and walked past her into the apartment.

"Mommy, where are my flippers? Have you seen my blue T-shirt? See what I'm taking with me." *O, Stefan, always the talker and so much fun. My little Louki, holding my hand. No questions, only me.*

"Have you put your things together for the trip, Louki? No? OK, just let me put my things down, then I'll look in at Stefan and come to you." Louki nodded, her gaze fixed to the floor, but she didn't let go.
Els freed her fingers and slipped into her room. She closed the door gently.

"Bart. Will you get the diving gear from the closet?" Her husband sat on the bed taking off his shoes. "Bart. Did you hear me?"

"Of course. I know my job."

His voice sounded bitter to her ears. Did he know why she was late?

She sat next to him and examined her hands. "I'm glad to get away, Bart. We've both been too busy for each other." That was her truth. What was his? A small bed in a small room, Els next to him. Love in the morning. Love at night. He wanted more, but he would be satisfied with that. He stood up. "I'll get started."

That night he dreamed he was making love to Els. They were not in their beds. They were flying. Slow motion flight, he drifting toward her, she always just out of reach. He touched her toes with his fingertips, she propelled herself a distance beyond his hands; he flew beside her and kissed her belly, she gathered strength and kicked away, freeing herself from him. She lingered, elusive; he moved onto her, they tumbled through space, their bodies two parallel lines in simultaneous flight, their arms, hands and legs free in the void, their faces one in rapture.

"Oh," he moaned softly.

"What's wrong?" she whispered.

"Nothing, nothing, I just had a dream, go back to sleep."

"Is it morning yet? Do we have to get up?"

Bart checked the clock. "No, it's only four. We still have a few hours."

Els turned over. Bart felt his cock stiffen. Shit. Els would have none of him in the middle of the night. Maybe, he rationalized. They were on vacation. He turned toward her and began to stroke her belly and her breasts. "Umm, not now Bart... tired." She spoke so softly he could hardly hear. She sighed heavily and was asleep again.

He rolled over on his back, letting his erection wilt and looking at the ceiling. The pose was not unfamiliar. He spent many nights like this, before lovemaking, after, and without, playing back scenes from work, conversations with Els, once in a while trying to make sense of a dream. Nothing difficult to understand in this one. They were flying, a nice sensation, even though she had resisted his touch at first. He savored the dream's ending. The only time he had her all to himself. And look how happy she was. As happy as he. Wasn't she? He turned away from her and closed his eyes. Their bodies were positioned spine to spine, the reverse of their bodies in his dream. Fortunately for him, Bart fell asleep before he noticed.

Here were these people, complete strangers, and if someone were to say, "That's not how I see them," worse yet, if the Dutch family were to read this and laugh, "We're nothing like this, nothing at all," I'd have shouted them down. I was right; I knew I was. Or if not right, passionate. It pleased me to be passionate about this couple, and to explore their passion. I'm at an age now where passion isn't as important to me as it was when I was younger. For years, I was ruled by sexual passion. It's not like that now.

I don't want to be done with passion. I don't want to be done with curiosity, or intense feeling or even pain. All those sensations are part of me. I'm afraid that as I grow older my emotions, like my physical characteristics, will melt into an indistinguishable mass, my chin part of my chest, my eyes part of my cheeks, my curiosity part of my boredom, and passion a dream I remember but can't bring to life.

I thought about this as I stared out at the Red Sea and waited for the Dutch family to come back.

The Sinai was hot. As they made their way toward the diving camp, the family kept the car windows rolled down. Soon, they were all covered in a fine dust. They had taken this drive before, visiting the diving club two or three times since arriving in Cairo, lured by its simplicity, the abundance of showy fish among the coral, the ease of diving there. Els never got used to the Sinai's mountains: huge, hulking creatures that hugged the road and rose on either side, red brown, devoid of vegetation. These were the most masculine mountains she had ever seen. No Swiss Alps of cottages and wildflowers, they were mountains to test the wills of prophets.

Stefan looked out his window. *Last time I saw camels. And Bedouins. Daddy told me about them, how they live in the desert and move from place to place. They don't like big cities. I like the robes the men wear. I hope, I hope, I hope I see camels.* He crossed his fingers and made a wish.

Louki sat huddled in the corner. She hugged her knees to her chest and rested her head on her knees, stroking her blanket against her face, sucking her thumb. *Look at Mommy in the front seat next to Daddy. Mommy loves me. Stefan loves me. Mommy loves Daddy. Daddy loves Mommy.* Louki repeated this equation to herself many times a day. Its familiarity gave it authority. It anchored her in the world. She didn't know that the equation on which she based her life didn't add up.

Bart was grateful the wind was too strong to make speaking easy. The children were quiet. Were they sleeping? He glanced at Stefan in the rearview mirror. In doing so, he caught a look at himself. He straightened his back allowing him to see his face beneath his sunglasses. The jaw he usually clenched was relaxed, even slack, making him look a little stupid, he thought. The face he ordinarily showed the world was stern. Some inner discipline was necessary to control his feelings. He couldn't hold his daughter without sobbing, he was sure.

The wind reminded Els of the Nile Valley. The land along the river, a dark, rich brown. It was windy along the roads that crossed the Valley of Kings. Els boarded her horse there, in a farmer's stable. As often as she could get away, she took the train south, first waiting with multitudes of tourists on the platform in Cairo and disembarking with them, ten hours later in Luxor. The tourists went by bus up the long road to the tombs of Ramses and Hatshepsut. She had seen these once, but they didn't interest her. She took a rattletrap taxi ten minutes into the countryside to the farm where she boarded her horse, Juweel. There she changed into riding clothes, ate a quick lunch supplied by the farmer's wife and hurried out to the stable. She saddled and mounted her horse. Juweel was always skittish at first. She had to calm him with softly-spoken words-goed, Juweel, daar, daar zachtjes maar meisje-patting his neck, walking him slowly out the gate and down the road when she saw he was ready.

He walked first, then trotted, then cantered. She held her seat confidently, gripping the animal's muscular body between her legs. She didn't worry about the horse, its feelings, its hidden pains. The horse gave her nothing to feel guilty about. When they had been out an hour or so, and if the day was not too hot, Els gave the horse the touch that meant, "Gallop." The animal always responded as if he, like Els, had been waiting for that moment. He picked up his pace and lengthened his stride. The path fell away from his hoofs; he stretched out his neck, and without any urging from Els, he flew. Faster than the Cairo train, faster than the wind, Els let herself imagine. She bent over his neck, crooning, yes, my beauty, yes, you beautiful creature, go, go, go, my lovely animal. Her red-brown hair streamed behind her like a banner.

This was her pleasure and she never invited Bart or the children to join her.

It was early in the evening before the family returned. I was in my room, putting on shorts and shirt for dinner when I heard Stefan saying something in Dutch. I opened my door and saw Bart and Els going into their room. Stefan had his arms full of fins and masks, which he laid next to his parents' door. He headed toward his room, followed by Louki, who, as always, walked several paces behind, her chin resting on her chest, her arms clutching her blanket.

No time then for conversation. I was disappointed. After a few minutes, I went to dinner with my friends. That night we were a raucous group. My friends' children and their friends joined us. Ages eighteen to twenty-three, all Israelis, they were young, strong and outspoken. Depending on their comfort with English they spoke to me a little or a lot. It didn't matter. I was dining al fresco in a Bedouin palace hung with rugs and multi-colored camel halters. I was on land's edge, at the tip of the Sinai Peninsula, twenty feet from the Red Sea, at the crossroads of the world, with friends I hadn't seen in many years. I was drunk with excitement at what I would discover next about the Dutch family, who were oblivious of any interest in them at all.

Much later, I stumbled back to my room. The lights were out; the doors were closed in all the rooms in the semicircle except for mine. My euphoria was winding down; I wanted to sleep.

Sometime later, I awoke when I heard a door open and the sound of soft footfalls on concrete. Then, silence. Someone walking up to the bathroom? I wanted to know who it was. I slipped a shirt over my nightgown and stepped outside my room. The door to Els and Bart's room was slightly ajar. I tiptoed to the end of the common area and peered down to the sea. The moon was full, illuminating the beach. Myriad cocoons of rugs held sleeping vacationers lured to the water's edge by the night's heat. I knew who had emerged from Els and Bart's room and where he was.

The day had not disappointed Bart, only the night. After leaving the diving club, they had snorkeled and swam in two dive spots that his boss had recommended. When the sun began to set, they ate a quick dinner in Sharm al Sheikh and returned to the diving club. He knew the children were worn out. Finally, he'd have time alone with Els. They were only in their room for a few minutes when Els said she was tired and was going to bed.

He tried not to stare while she took off her shorts and shirt and hung her bathing suit from a wall peg. She slid under the covers, her body so slim, she barely raised a lump in the blanket. He straightened out the snorkeling gear and readied the dive equipment for the morning. He sat outside, smoked a cigarette and watched the full moon rise, feeling its beauty like a smooth pebble in his throat. Opening the door to their room quietly, he pulled the covers away and lay down next to his wife. He put his arms around her and, like the night before, began to stroke her body. This night, she didn't say anything; she backed closer to the wall, out of his reach.

Finally, "I'm sorry, Bart."

"What's to be sorry?" He said. "There's always tomorrow." This time, he turned his back to her first and fell asleep immediately.

He woke with a start. In his dream, he had held liquid in his cupped hands, marveling at the miracle of finding fresh water in the desert. Suddenly the water turned from clear to rust, trickling through his fingers so fast he was unable to staunch the flow. His eyes open, he was at first so frightened, he couldn't move. Slowly, his heart returned to its normal rhythm. Els slept on. She didn't move when he pulled on his shorts and opened the door.

He wandered down to the water's edge and turned his steps toward the stunted palm tree where they had placed their blanket that morning. He walked close to the tree and estimated the space the blanket would have taken. He closed his eyes and saw Els sitting on the blanket alone, without Stefan or Louki or him. He opened his eyes, and by moonlight, counted out the steps until he stood where she would have sat earlier that day. He sat down there, sure that the sand still held her warmth.

Els heard Bart leave. She sat up in bed, tears streaming down her face. She held herself as she had often seen Louki do, her head hunched forward into her chest, clutching her blanket close to her face. She rocked back and forth. This life was ending. She didn't will it, but it was ending, nevertheless. She searched her mind for the reason she knew this to be true and saw Josef's smiling face. She knew the next time she rode Juweel, Josef would be riding beside her.

I turned away before Bart headed back to his room. I grieved for him hearing what I imagined Els would tell him tonight, or tomorrow. I didn't think she'd wait long. This couple, so young, and at least in my imagination, so passionate. They were tortured. I could tell them that in twenty years, they wouldn't care. All this would be behind them. They either would have stayed together and wonder why they ever found one another so mysterious, or they would have split apart, crumbling Stefan and Louki's childhoods into pieces the children would spend their lives trying to make whole.

The Beating of Wings

We lived in a land of dreams, I often told Donkor, my husband. Papyrus grew like dense forests next to our river, the Nile, a home to fish and fowl. The land we farmed was rich and fertile, always willing to give us the wheat and millet, oranges and pomegranates we ate in abundance.

We were raising our three children near the plain where a great pyramid was being constructed. Though we did not hear the crack of whips, we were not unaware of the slaves' suffering. Donkor's job was to keep the slaves working. He hated the role he played in their lives. There was little he could do, he told us, except to inflict as little pain as possible. We tried to teach our children to care for life, a lesson we often impressed upon our eldest son, Babak. We had named him "little father," in the hope that he would pass our words on to his own children someday.

Babak sighed as he turned in his sleep. I awoke to see Donkor open the door shortly after sunrise. Even as my eyes opened to a new day, I sensed something amiss. The light, which usually shined directly into our dwelling at daybreak, was muted, barely brighter than the darkness. My husband must have sensed the change also because I saw him pause. At that moment, the light was extinguished, as if all the oil lamps in all the rooms of the world had been put out.

He said, "It is night." I heard a tremor in his voice.

We had witnessed a blood-poisoned Nile and then seen swarms of lice, pests and insects descend upon us, killing our livestock and ravaging our fields. After masses of frogs had risen out of the Nile, we were forced to retreat to our houses. When we emerged the following day, the bodies of dead frogs had lain like a putrid carpet around our feet. Now, this darkness.

My husband left. He had to work. The children slept on. I stared at our ceiling straw. What good was it to rise if the sun had not? Donkor returned, breathing heavily, as if he had been running. "I have gone the length of the village, all the way to the Nile," he said. "There is no work to be done without light. No one knows why the darkness is so black and so thick."

"How can darkness be thick?" I asked.

"Come. See for yourself."

As I emerged from the dwelling into the daynight, I felt covered as if by a shroud. The house next to ours was barely visible although it was only a few steps away. "Donkor," I called. My voice was muffled. I stuck my hand out in front of me, thinking I would grasp something solid in the air. But when I closed my fist, my palm was empty.

Babak and his younger brother and sister continued to sleep. "I'm not going to wake them," I said to Donkor. "Why frighten them?"

We both went back to bed. In other times, we would have taken the rare holiday to enjoy each other's bodies. Instead, we lay as if dead until we fell asleep.

The sun was our God. Its rise and descent had marked our days. Without light, we were adrift.

Time passed slowly as we huddled in our house, afraid of the darkness outside, of who or what we would encounter on the road. Our children rarely left our sides. Only our animals carried on with the rhythm of their lives. In the end, it was our cow, lowing insistently, that gave order to our days. By letting us know she needed to be milked, we also knew when a day began and when it ended.

We counted the passing of three days that way when, at last, we were awakened by the sun. I followed Donkor into the road where our neighbors had gathered. We did not rejoice that we were able to begin a new day. Instead, we looked into each other's faces and saw fear. We stood together only a moment before returning to our houses.

We Egyptians lost more than days of work while we sat in darkness. We lost faith in our gods and, although none of us dared to speak of it, in our Pharaoh. The strange happenings that had begun when the Nile turned to blood had finally come to this. Each time we were plagued with a disaster— for surely, it would take us more than a season to plant and sow the millet, barley, figs and pomegranates that had been destroyed—we expected the Pharaoh to create an assembly or send a spokesperson to explain. But no one had come, and we were forced to depend on rumors.

One rumor was repeated more often than others: Moses, an aged Israelite who had been raised in the Pharaoh's home, had petitioned Pharaoh, demanding, "Allow the Israelite slaves to leave your kingdom." When Pharaoh refused, Moses's god had caused the unnatural events we had witnessed.

What's more, the hardships we Egyptians felt did not befall the Israelites. The water in their jugs continued to be pure while ours had been polluted with blood. During the long daynight, the sun had risen and fallen on their houses as always.

The darkness had lifted, but we did not carry on as if nothing were amiss. Each of us, every Egyptian neighbor and villager in all our land, feared yet another catastrophe—one that would make even the worst we had already known appear small by comparison.

Donkor, I could see, had been as unnerved by the long daynight as I. One evening, he raised his hand to strike me. He had never struck me, and before this time, I never thought he would. I told my son, Babak, that I would fetch our water and asked my husband to come with me. Though I was alarmed by his threat of violence, I allowed my steps to fall into his pace as if we were the young people we had been when we first married. We reached the Nile as the sun fell below the horizon. Hidden by the reeds, I whispered to my husband, "The Israelites' god will protect us when...." I could not give voice to what I feared would take place next.

Donkor looked around. Seeing no one, he said, "Why do you believe?"

"When the Israelite barber, Reuben, begged us to protect his first-born son from Pharaoh's soldiers, we risked our safety. We helped him. We even lied to our neighbors, saying the boy was the newborn child of your uncle whose wife had died in childbirth."

"Yes," he said. "No one questioned us though the infant looked nothing like either of us." My husband looked more hopeful. He had always liked the boy. "And when the child was three years old, we returned him to the Israelites. Their god will know what we did. We will be safe."

Telling this story to each other reassured us. My step felt lighter on our way home.

Dusk was coming on the next day when Masika, our neighbor, knocked at our door. She was a small-boned woman who carried herself with dignity. Her appearance was always in good order, her graying hair in place under a head covering, her dress always clean.

That evening, I hardly recognized her. Her hair was unkempt, and I detected the unfamiliar smell of sweat.

"Masika, what happened?" I asked.

"Your husband. Is he here?"

"No, he looked downcast when he came home. He was better off being with his fellows. I sent him off. What happened?" I asked again.

"My brother who works at the palace—he heard the Pharaoh's advisers say the Israelites are smearing their animals' blood on their doorway posts and lintels. My brother went to see for himself. It is true." Deep furrows in Masika's brow and around her eyes marked her usually placid face. Her hands, always engaged in a chore, twisted on each other in agitation.

"Blood? Why does it matter where they put it?" I said.

She cried out. "Don't you see? The blood is a sign."

I had never before heard Masika raise her voice. "Be calm," I said. "We don't know what this means." I tried to place my hand on her shoulder, but she shook it off.

"*I* know." She spoke with authority, this woman whose voice I had rarely heard until this day.

She would not meet my eyes. I stared stupidly at her, even as I felt my heart pound in my chest. I, too, had imagined the worst that could befall us. My husband struck down, or the Nile overflowing and drowning us all. I had dreamed it but was not ready for Masika's panic. She saw something that I did not.

She said, "Now, the Israelites' god will use all his power against the Pharaoh until the Israelites are set free."

Night had drawn around us, moonless and still. It was not the thick darkness the Israelites' god had brought, but every night brings its terrors, I had learned long ago.

"What is left for their god to do?" I implored.

I heard my children inside the house, the high-pitched voice of my youngest and the lower voice of Babak, who would soon be a man. "Oh no," I said before Masika had a chance to answer. I knew what she would have told me. "Oh no," I said again. I shut the door. I wanted to bar the entrance to the pain that I knew would follow.

I gathered my children into my arms and rocked them as I had when they were small. Only the younger two allowed me to hold them. My beloved Babak stepped away and stood looking at me as if I were as strange as the happenings that he, too, had witnessed.

I fed them their evening meal, not waiting for my husband to return. I moved as if I were sleepwalking. I knew the Israelites' god because I knew our own. Gods must be obeyed.

My children went to bed. I lay in the dark, waiting for my husband, for what would come next. My children were breathing rhythmically in their sleep.

In the distance, I heard a loud *swish-swish-swish* as if a hundred giant birds were beating their wings in unison. The wings' sound became louder. Grief-stricken cries tore the night, coming closer to our village minute by minute. I leaped up. I cracked open the door and peered into the night sky. Not birds, but scores of small, winged creatures hovered above the village, making the sky look like a live, quivering mass. I wanted to cover my ears but I would not give in even as I heard the screams grow louder.

In minutes, the world was engulfed in a cacophony of sound. A whir of wings became a shriek as the creatures dove from sky to earth and back again. Silence followed for a moment, broken by our villagers' anguished wails. Over one house, the next, and the next. All too quickly, screams arose from every house in the village. I could not escape. My children could not escape. In the screams, I heard a kind of suffering I had begged my gods never to inflict on us.

And then, I heard the frantic beating of wings hover over our house.

Twenty-Six Photographs | Bill Davis

Black and White

I don't have a specific aesthetic for my photography. None of it is staged or posed and most of the photos are of nature. My technique is a nexus of fast twitch finger muscles combined with a willingness to carry a heavy camera with a reasonably good telephoto lens to some out-of-the-way places: East Africa, India, Thailand, Mexico, the Galapagos Islands, Nepal, Japan. The photos in the book represent the thousands I have snapped over the years.

Birds in their natural setting are very compelling to me. Getting a good picture is almost a matter of luck. Someone who knows much more about photography than I told me that for a bird photo to be successful the bird's eye needs to be in focus. Occasionally I succeed. I find other kinds of animals compelling as well. East African fauna, reptiles, almost anything that moves.

By far my favorite photo is of the gray whale calf surfacing next to our panga at San Ignacio Lagoon. Captured his/her eye in the rippling water. Clearly taking us in with that big marine mammal brain. There is real sentience there. The calf was with its mother—spending the last week or so at San Ignacio before heading on its 6,000-mile migration north to the Bering Sea.

Besides animals, I'm interested in the built environment, especially in patterns and repetitions. The stone walls and steps in Kumbhalgarh, India; the patterns made by a farmer plowing with his ox in Nepal; the repetition of stone lanterns in a garden in Kyoto, Japan. All these capture my attention and beg to be photographed.

Essentially, I belong to the blind squirrel school of photography: namely, just as a blind squirrel will find a nut on occasion, so I will take a good photograph every so often. I've never taken any lessons in photography but have owned a 35mm camera since 1965 when I was 19 years old and stationed with the U.S. Army in Japan.

On the Wing

Twenty-Four Poems | Marie Pal-Brown

The Intertwining

I think of poems as dreams. Like sleep-time dreams, poems, too, rise from unknown depths. Both are mysterious.

As uninvited visitors, sleep-time dreams find their cues in daytime events and spin their stories camouflaged in arcane language.

Poems are invited guests. We welcome them, or perhaps they seek us out. They become visible in the imagery and musings that come upon us during waking reality. The sight of a simple flower, exposing its essence; a cloud in the sky, revealing its hidden spirit. In the poem, what is literal and what is metaphoric magically merge.

I chose the 24 poems printed here from six of my collections written between 1997 and 2021: *Venice Garden Poems, Your Broad Hands Touching Me, Phoenix Journal, Lagoon Poems, Abbey Poems,* and a last poem that stands on its own. They are witness to my journey of literal experience intertwining with metaphor.

From *Venice Garden Poems*

In the spring of 1997, having neglected my Venice, California, garden for years, ideas began to take shape in my mind that gradually led me to design and plant a seaside cottage garden. Terraced along meandering paths through myriad flower beds, a pond at one end and the old queen palm at the center, it became the view from my study desk.

What I didn't know then was that at the same time that my own garden was becoming a reality, my mother—then in her early eighties and already in declining health—had abruptly retired from tending the garden of my childhood home along the Rhine River.

These turns of events, mysteriously synchronistic in nature, gave me pause for both sadness and gratitude. It was as if my mother's sacrifice had been an offering to me, making me the inheritor of her lifelong passion.

And thus I began working on a series of garden poems. A number of them were written in her memory after her passing in 2001.

Hibiscus Flowers Trembling Above the Old Buddha

Sun and rain have bleached the Buddha's burgundy cloak,
now sandstone white and mossy in the shoulder folds.
His belly button has been washed away. The years have pinched
the mouth into a toothless grin, yet the cheeks are Buddha-chubby still.

His lidless eyes squint at his reflection rippling
on the pond's surface,
while two swollen-bellied guppies
nibble at a blood-red hibiscus flower floating in the deep.
Air bubbles bob drunkenly on the brackish water,
burst and vanish, leaving nothing
but—for a moment—rings of yellowish foam.

There is no mystery in the decaying Buddha,
the unending parade of bubbles imploding,
the hibiscus flowers that last for a single day—
only in the prayer to a god forever imagined,
said over and over, regardless.

Seasons

for David Pal

A white-crowned sparrow hops from branch to branch in the peach tree. It flaps and fluffs its wings for warmth this chilly Christmas Eve morning. Then flies away.

The tree stands winter naked. One leaf curls from its topmost branch; another hangs twisted from a sawed-off limb.

I think of summers when the peach tree bore abundant fruit. More stayed dwarfed, hard as rocks after an early-season spurt; others were foraged in the night by possums nesting in the compost heap.

I would watch you through the kitchen window, as you took measure of the fruit's slow swelling. Always, you would wait to pick them until their color was peach perfect, their firmness just barely giving to the touch. Cradling them in your palms, like fragile Christmas balls, you would carry them inside, put them on the kitchen counter.

Already, next season's buds have sprung from the old growth. Come spring, I will witness another year's flushed bloom—without you.

All Souls' Day

Memento mori populate my garden:

Star succulents for my father. He fell in battle at the Russian front fifty-seven years ago, come Christmas.

Stargazer lilies, spent but for their stalks, for Linus, Bettina's infant boy, named at birth for Linus of Thebes, the youth struck dead by Heracles with his lyre. The name a prophecy, as it were.

Three miniature rose bushes along the border of the lower flower bed for Wolf Friederich, who instilled in me the love of language.

Calla lilies for Sigrid McPherson. She broke her neck falling—some say, jumping—from her second-story window, leaving Rilke's *Book of the Hours* open to "When something of mine falls from a window."

A clay pot of red-fleshed aeonium succulents for Steve. "When you know the end is coming," he said the day before he died, "it's like free fall."

A tub of orange lantanas in gratitude to Edward Edinger and his work, *Anatomy of the Soul.*

Pekoe's grave near the garage wall. The wooden cutout of a black cat, in her memory, marks the spot where we buried her.

Abrubt gusts of wind. Palm fronds scrape against the trellis above the fence. An unsettling light washes over everything.

Rain Fell Overnight

The cloud-hung sky has erased
yesterday's reflection of the magnolia tree
against the stark white fence.

First rain since I planted it last November,
the week my mother died.
Tips of pale green leaves sprouting
on the tree's flower-studded branches.

My mother's likeness in the photo on my writing table
has eclipsed the face, waxen to the touch, I stroked
as she lay in her coffin.

By afternoon, the clouds will break up.
A tentative sun will quicken my garden.
Drawn on the fence, the shadow magnolia will return,
mimic the wind-dance of its earthbound counterpart.

All the while, the paint-chipped gnome from pre-WWI Germany
stands stolid, eyes mock-twinkling, fixed
on the blue narcissus flowering at his feet,
season after season.

The Vast Summer Has Gone by

Blanched sky. Gusts of wind tousle
the queen palm fronds. A patch of mackerel cloud
above the guesthouse warns that rain is near.

The Japanese maple is shedding
brown-stained and yellow-spotted leaves.
The rosebushes I planted in gratitude
for my beloved friend and teacher W. F.
bend under clusters of brimming pink.
A late daylily lifts its chalice to heaven.
Burgundy-blooming geraniums spill over clay pots.

My work this early autumn
has been to prepare the garden for winter—
dig up the dahlia tubers to replant mid-spring,
deadhead the gold coin daisies, weed clover
and dandelion, prune the shrubs,
cut back the perennials, turn the soil,
mindful of corms and hidden shoots,
of lowly earthworms, too, making mulch
to sweeten the ground.

Today, I sweep the storm drain, unclog the grates.
Then wait for the rains to come.

February Heat Wave, California

for Bettina Wildling

Unseasonal heat. The magnolia tree has grown
a full crown of leaves too soon this year.
At the edge of the lower flower bed,
a lavender-dusted rose has burst into early bloom.

White butterflies skim across the garden.
A spring bird's love-laden song rings
from the peach tree's greening branches.
The air smells of summer drought.

In late fall, I planted a grouping of stargazer lily bulbs
for Linus, my friend's dead infant boy. Now, overnight,
short stalks of pale blades, wrapped onion tight,
have pierced through the hardened soil.

Morning Prayer

I light the Virgin of Guadalupe candle
I bought on Olvera Street
in the Pueblo heart of Los Angeles,

stir the hundred or so printed cards of daily counsel
that I keep in a bowl on my desk.
One falls to the floor, face up. "Pray," it reads.
I draw another: "Give thanks."

Outside the French doors, hazy light
bathes my garden,
The sun is a milky disk above the roofs.

Three last blossoms, the size of saucers,
the ivory of a bridal gown,
are left among the bounteous
leafage of the camellia bush
my mother planted years ago.

The magnolia that marks her passing
is now a winter-bare skeleton
drawn against the white-washed wall,
its branches knobbed with furry buds.

This morning, I see the garden
with my mother's eyes,

her hands working the soil.

October

Dawn casts a wash of grey onto the lavender walls.
Shadows huddle in the folds of my eiderdown.
In the painting above the dresser,
the reclining nude, her harlequin lover's gaze
upon her body, looks robbed
of desire's flush in the low light.

I take off my night clothes,
stand facing the mirror.
Still shrouded in semidarkness,
the diffuse image
of a much younger woman
slowly comes into view,
her skin flawless, her breasts gently sloped.

I wait for nature's daily sleight of hand
when night turns into day:

Leafy patterns take shape in the weave
of the prayer rug beneath the window.
Glow of sunrise tinges
the painting's dark background,
arouses the nude, blushes her cheeks.

In the mirror, I recognize the older woman:
skin winter pale, left breast cancer scarred.

I put on a flannel robe, warm slippers,
step outside into my garden.

I walk along the terraced paths,
through the end-of-season splurge of color—
marigolds, chrysanthemums, asters.

The last of the roses flaunt their innermost petals,
still fleshy pink, while the outermost petals
look withered, their color gone.

Come winter, I will prune the rosebushes
to all but skeletal shapes,
gather their leaves and stems for the compost bin.

From *Your Broad Hands Touching Me*

In the mid-nineties, I met my future husband in the writing workshop of the late Holly Prado. Neither of us would have imagined that, in time, a mutual respect for each other's writing would lead to a love affair, certainly not a marriage. But a moment came when, almost in spite of ourselves, we changed course—from colleagues to friends to lovers to husband and wife.

Sometime into our relationship, we began writing poetry to each other that chronicled and celebrated the story of our courtship.

Mine became the collection, *Your Broad Hands Touching Me,* and his, *A Great Shook Bone.*

The six poems I chose for this section start with the very first one in the collection, written in Germany, in 1998, and end with the final poem, written in the summer of 2005—celebrating a still timid beginning to an eventual life together.

I'm indebted to my husband, Garrett Brown, for the inspiration that brought these poems to life.

Love Letter from Germany

I dream I write a poem,
the words black on pure white paper.

Sitting in the tall grass of a summer meadow,
I read it to you,
the love poem I feared could not be written.

At the edge of waking and sleep, it fades.

What remains is desire: a hunger, never stilled,
more now as I am six thousand miles away.

From the window of my girlhood bedroom,
I daydream into my mother's garden,
watch blackbirds on the weeping birch
preen their feathers,
soar high on the wind.

Mother's Day

1.
This morning, I sit in my garden,
waiting for the sun
to touch the magnolia bush I planted
in my mother's memory.
I wear her favorite plaid robe, read aloud
Friedrich Schiller's *Das Lied von der Glocke*
—"The Song of the Bell"—
the poem she recited our last summer together,
foretelling, as she spoke the lines,
her own death just months away.
Von dem Dom / Schwer und bang /
Tönt die Glocke / Grabgesang.
—From the tower / Tolls the bell, /
Dull and heavy / The funeral knell.

2.
The florist has delivered a dozen salmon-colored tulips
with a note from my son Jeremy.
From my daughter Daniela, a pretty basket
—in it a garden book, dahlia bulbs, a bottle of bath soak.
A card from my older daughter Alison will arrive
tomorrow. "Your love is always with me," it will say.

3.
In a few hours you and I will drive south
to San Juan Capistrano, to spend a few days
at the Seaside Inn, Room 33, *La Felicidad*
—the honeymoon suite, the receptionist will say—
a balcony overlooking the waves.

You will give me two gifts, making sure I know
these are not Mother's Day gifts:
a necklace of silver strands, moonstone
and jade-tipped, that will dangle
into my cleavage and, later,
when we make love, feather your chest.
Also, *Vita Nova* by Louise Glück,
because of the last line in the title poem:
"it is still spring, it is still meant tenderly."

I Cannot Bear the Thought

You say the rose you stole for me
from a bush on your neighbor's porch
smells like an orange. You hand it to me,
a mischievous smile on your face,
during our Sunday morning tryst.
You say no more of the rose,
nothing of its beauty, pink and vulva-smooth,
only: "It smells like an orange."

Once you've left in the early afternoon
I am alone on the crumpled sheets,
dim light filtering through the drawn curtains.

I touch the purple-kissed bruise
you've left on my right breast,
turn to the rose, still glorious
—though its edges have already faded—
standing in a glass on my nightstand
where you left it for me.

Once the rose has withered, I will gather its petals,
put them to dry in the Chinese bowl
on my kitchen table, along with the petals
of all the other roses you have given me over time.

If it so happens that you no longer
come to me on Thursdays and Sundays,
or any other day, the watercolor you titled
I'm with you
—a man and a woman entwined
on the cross—
will still hang on my bedroom wall,
and I'll carry the memory
of this bruise near my heart.

Although I cannot bear the thought.

Lenbachhaus, Munich

We view the paintings of the *Blaue Reiter* group—
Franz Marc, Kandinsky, Paul Klee,
and my favorite, Gabriele Münter,
her painting *Sinnende,* of a woman musing.
We're enchanted by the boldness of colors and lines, lost
until summoned back by the shuffling of feet on the parquet floor,
the low hum in the gallery.

Downstairs, we walk through darkened rooms,
optical-illusion exhibits of light, shimmering and vanishing,
ephemeral, as are we.

On the staircase wall, a poster of Pia Stadtbäumer's show
Androgyn/Gynander, 1993—life-size clay statues
hanging from wires, crown of skull to ceiling,
male genitalia paired with female breasts,
slitted mounds with muscle-bound pectorals.

We leave in late dusk and light winter rain.
Then turn back, facing the façade:
high above the portal, like a modern-day oracle,
blue neon letters spell out in English

"You can imagine the opposite"

I look into your rain-misted face,
the words on the wall in the periphery of my vision.
I want to halt this moment
that has already slipped into the past.
Our love, like all loves, temporal
and timeless.

Deck View, 8 Nilson Way, Truro

for GMB

The sun's late rays flush the pine branches crimson.
The road looks bathed in purple.
Tiger lilies on the embankment
bloom into orange trumpets.

Most days, I am blind to the forest's fiery
spectacle at dusk.

Today, I'm blessed with the innocent's vision:

Pines ablaze, sky shimmering
on the ripples of the pond below,
embankment of a thousand fires.

Like the Hands of a Workingman

1.
A dark Cape Cod sky has swallowed
the tree tops. The rain will last for hours.
Warm humidity fogs the cottage windows,
moistens my tanned skin.

Propped up naked against a pile of pillows,
I read aloud from Gary Eberle's *Sacred Time,*
the passage about sex as ritual
suspending the measured hours.

"Stay that way," you say, and fetch
your drawing pad from the kitchen table.
You join the pen-point to the page.
Your eyes are harnessed to the edges of my body
as is your hand to the contour it draws.
A simultaneous tingle traces
the corresponding line on my skin.
Your gaze moves along the boundary
that outlines my body's form.
I am
both flesh and tracing, both model and muse.

2.
Late afternoon, we stand near the ocean's edge
at Ballston Beach, alone but for a fisherman
reeling in his line. Our bodies glisten
in the weakening sunlight.
Facing the waves, standing side by side, we move
through our evening yoga practice—
sun salutations, lunges, warrior poses, tree.
We finish, hands folded in pose-perfect *Namaste,*
the hollows of our palms, cathedral spaced.

3.
We return to Southern California—
you to Los Feliz, I to my Venice house and garden

where there's a problem with roots in the sewer pipe.
A ditch needs to be dug to expose and mend the cracks.
A job you offer to do on your weekend visit.

Saturday morning, you mark off the area,
position your feet, mindful not to trample the plants.
You clasp the shovel-handle, grip sure.
You push the shovel into the ground,
lift, balance, turn, then tip blade-full
after blade-full into the wheelbarrow.

Delicately, to preserve the tender root ball,
you pull out a young palm near the offending pipe.

Sweat trickles down your temples.
You lean your forearms on the shovel's handle,
rub your sore hands, survey the morning's work,
pleased.

I think of lying with you on cool sheets,
your broad hands touching me.

From *Phoenix Journal*

Dearest to my heart is a series of poems interspersed among the entries of the *Phoenix Journal,* a journal I kept from 2005 to 2006, during the months I accompanied my younger daughter Daniela through a prolonged recovery after an illness. Reading through them, I found most of the poems too personal to present to a larger audience. Still, as a tribute to that time of hardship, uncertainty, tenderness and the eventual return of my daughter's health, I selected a poem of a walk we took together in the Phoenix desert.

"When you listen for it, there is nothing to hear" *

We walk in the early shadows of the Phoenix mountains,
my daughter's Sheltie pulling on her leash,
then dropping back, circling behind our feet as if to herd us.
The only sounds, the crunch of gravel on the path
and the tags on the dog's collar, jingling.

Dark patches of shale cloak the mountains' faces.
Ribbons of trails snake up to the peaks.
Giant saguaros on the lower slopes, survivors
from a past world, raise their arms into the windless air.

My daughter's health is frail, so we keep
to the gentler flats, walk at a measured pace,
follow a loop through spent desert grass.
We cross dry arroyos of rock and driftwood
washed up by last summer's monsoon.

I look up toward the mountains.
I plead for answers to questions I dare not ask.
My anxious glance strokes the scar,
still pink and welted, above the left temple
on my daughter's shaven head.

The mountains keep their silence.

*Tao Te Ching, Chapter 35

From *Lagoon Poems*

The first months after we moved into our Long Beach home on the eastern shore of the Colorado Lagoon, I would sit at my study window, looking out over our garden and, beyond it, the 18-acre expanse of an L-shaped body of water. I watched the water rise and fall, puzzled by the glassy surface appearing between tides. I observed the abundance of seabirds without knowing their names and habits; flying fish leaving ever-expanding rings across the ripples; umbrellas of jellyfish drifting below the surface near the footbridge; wetland plant life alien to my eye.

Beyond its visible beauty, the lagoon, its wildlife and landscape, would not open itself to me. It seemed painfully impenetrable. I cannot pinpoint the particular moment when it allowed me to enter its hidden depth, the moment it revealed its secrets. It was a gradual discovery, as finally, images and words met to create poetry.

Sunday Morning

Somewhere up the road, worshippers
trickle into St. Bartholomew's Church.

Along the lagoon, a pair of joggers,
bare shoulders glistening,
cheeks flushed.

The Southern magnolia trees lining the sidewalk
outside the house
shed their browning leaves to the earth.
They give themselves over to ever dying,
while growing virgin foliage, abundantly,
day in, day out.

I say my simple prayers to a silent God,
comes the echo of the voice that doubts.

Morris

Dawn. Light and dark mingle,
the sky is a dirty sheet.

The lagoon rests at slack water between the tides,
lays bare the eel grass along the shore.

From the front porch, I see a man in a green shirt
standing at the shore,
his curly-tailed pug on a leash.

Same man, same dog,
reflected upside down on the ripple-less surface.

Likewise the egret twinned in the water,
stalking morsels at the silty edge.

Mirror images of bearded palm trees hem the lagoon.
Morris Hayter, who built this 1950s house,
planted them to enhance the view.

Once, in a dream, he rang my doorbell,
jarring me out of midnight sleep.
He had been dead for years.

Still, I believe in dreamtime visits from the departed,
in the green-breasted hummingbird
of my mother's soul. Day by day, it hovers briefly
at my window, then disappears.

I toss a piece of junk mail addressed to Morris Hayter.
I listen in vain for the whoosh of wings.
The tide has turned. The water ripples.
The mirror worlds break into watery shards.

Late Afternoon in the Time of Corona

I sit musing at my study window.
The garden is bathed in cloud-reflected light,
the eucalyptus grove, the pepper tree, the California live oak—
none cast a shadow.

In the yin-yang-shaped patch of society garlic,
this year's first cluster of lavender stars sways on a single stalk.
The lowliest of plants in my garden, come June,
will flaunt a sea of color rising and falling
in the breeze from the lagoon.

A gossamer web floats among the mute chimes
on a shepherd's hook, abandoned
to wind and rain.

Just beyond the garden gate,
on the woodchip path along the lagoon,
a man passes. His son, perhaps fifteen,
follows a few steps behind.

I notice the boy's stumbling gait,
awkwardly tilted head.
A mask covers half his face.
His almond eyes are wide set and thick lidded.
He cocks his head, fixes his gaze,
as if he'd spied me here behind my window.

In a burst of grace, I glimpse the wondrous
parity of all creation:
voluptuous white iceberg roses along the fence;
the ginkgo tree, its spring-greening leaves;
two squirrels scurrying up the eucalyptus trunk.
And on the path, the father and his boy
passing by.

Advent, Colorado Lagoon

An angel wing hovers low in the December sky,
white cloud feathers bloom into golden embers
and mauve of another vanishing day.

Then wind brushes away the wing
and a darkening heaven swallows it whole.

I step out onto the living room deck:
a snowy egret swoops past, coots huddle
in the shallows along the shore.

Nine rafts, each a skeleton pyramid,
float on the lagoon's swelling body.

And then-a thousand bursts of light—
nine humble frames
become
nine dazzling Christmas trees

doubled
as their reflections quiver
upside down
in the rippling water.

I search the heavens for wings,
wait for angels to raise their trumpets.

From *Abbey Poems*

My first visit to St. Andrew's Abbey, a Benedictine monastery in the Mojave Desert of Southern California, goes back more than two decades. It was for a conference on the Marian poems by Rainer Maria Rilke. This was followed by many private as well as guided retreats. Eventually, under the mentorship of Fr. Francis Benedict, it led to taking my final vows as an oblate, a lay member of the monastery.

The three poems included here are a reflection of the movements of my soul as I continue the journey through the latter years of my life.

Dusk, St. Andrew's Abbey Retreat

On the grounds outside my room,
a clump of Joshua trees, gnarled
by heat and wind,
their trunks bearded with dead spines
the color of Mojave Desert dust,
spikes pointed
into a deep lavender sky.

Swaths of cloud turn a smeared red,
then ashen, as the sun dips
behind the gold-crusted cupolas
of the San Gabriel Mountains.

On the mission-style desk,
a frosted-glass Madonna—
she holds the Child.
Her robe, face, the Child's, too,
glow incandescent—made holy
by light from an ordinary lamp.

Winter Day, St. Andrew's Abbey

1.
After Lauds, the young monk kneads the soft wax
into the burning centers of the candles
before blowing out their flames.
He closes the book of Holy Scriptures,
from which earlier he read aloud a passage from *Isaiah*.
He carries the lectern to the far side of the monks' pews.
Passing the altar, he bows, then raises his eyes
to the Mexican folk art crucifix.

The worshippers gone, only I remain kneeling in the pew.
Sunlight bursts through the stained-glass windows.
From the organ, a final postscript crescendos.
Then, silence.
The young monk turns. He meets my gaze.

2.
The sinking sun has smudged the sky
with purple and orange above the foothills.
A cloud, diaphanous as a widow's veil,
spreads an ashen cast over what had been the apple orchard.

I cringe, remembering the howling of chainsaws
waking me this morning at daybreak.
Now, tree stumps and gnarly roots, yanked from the earth,
lie sprawled beside open craters, amid tangles
of dismembered winter branches and sawn logs.

On the far side of the ravaged landscape,
the young monk, hands tucked under his habit,
wanders among the ghostly shapes,
pausing at each, as if paying his last respects to the trees.

I want to cry out, "Was this God's will?"

An abandoned bird's nest, wedged in the crook
of a severed trunk, has survived unscathed.
I pry it from the scabbed bark.
Cradling the remains in both hands, I climb
the slope toward my room.
A breeze grabs a few thin twigs and feathers,
floats them down to the sandy, upturned loam.

"Enclose, my heart, this blessed wonder"*

for Fr. Angelus Echeverry

1.
What lasts, if anything?

Could it be that Christ's Sermon on the Mount
goes on echoing through the universe,
after two thousand years?

I heard with my own ears
Bach's "Schließe, mein Herze, dies selige Wunder."*
sung on Christmas Eve in the abbey chapel,
four hundred years after it first rang
through St. Thomas Cathedral.

2.
The holy ones, their words
live through eternity.

The luminous ones, their works
endure through time and space.

Nothing, not even the ordinary,
fades into nothingness.

Feast of all that is, that was, and that shall be.

*"Aria," *Christmas Oratorio* by J.S. Bach

Last Poem

Night after George Floyd's Murder

Dreamscape of endless graves—so many—
across the continent.
The earth is dark, moist.

I'm tending potted mother-in-law tongues,
row upon row upon row,
striped blades, long and sturdy
like fingers, pointing to the sky.

In the overcast dawn,
the same pots, now empty, dot the fields, a hundred million
and more, from the Pacific to the Atlantic.

I scoop up soil and fill the pots.
Into each center, I press a split-open seed,
sprinkle them with rain and holy water.

Sunflowers on sturdy stalks shoot up, fiercely,
their petals a dazzling yellow, their centers a speckled brown.

I watch as they grow:
a sea of sunflowers swaying in the May breeze.

My weeping wakes me.

Tooth and Claw

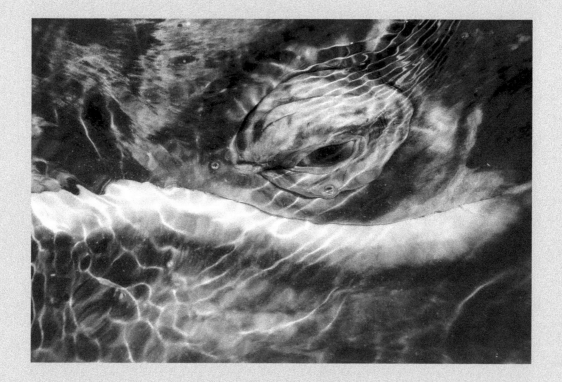

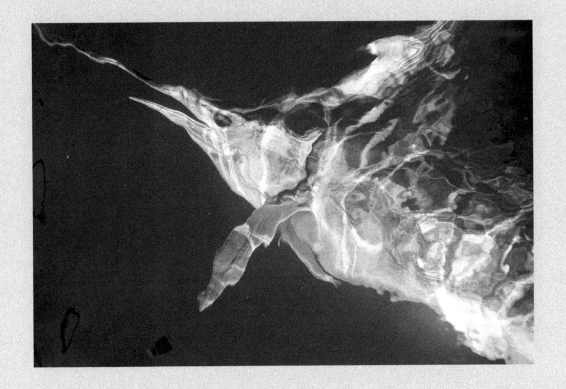

Three Stories | Garrett M. Brown

Tell-Tale

Re-reading and re-working these pieces, I realized that all three speak to my own immersion and love of the creative process.

"The Tragedy of Modern Man In 3 Acts... By Garry Brown" is a kind of 'origin' story: consumed with sports and studies in high school, I was not a natural in either, but what I've come to see as an "effort guy", ready to hustle and do hard work. My love of language, drama, story was mostly hidden from me through high school into college, with now and then a rare spontaneous expression, as this "epic play" seemed to be.

In 2020, I'd been reading Nora Ephron's wonderfully tender, funny, anecdotal personal essays when "My New Yorker Cover" emerged. It, too, speaks to beginnings and the whole assortment of my then (and now) creative intrigues: books, drawings, journal-keeping, poem-making, touching on the mysteries of acting and playwriting. Though I was a 22-year-old college graduate turned orderly at Courtland Gardens Nursing Home, I was reading Robert Frost and considering which road might be taken.

While the first two stories are what I call hybrid-memoirs, namely, memory mixed with a few fictional touches, "Riot Act" is an extrapolation into pure story. I did play four years of college basketball (after an abortive freshman football season), and I did receive a letter from the Dallas Cowboys football scout, Gil Brandt, asking for my statistics. Also, there was a pre-med student-athlete at our small northeastern college, Doug Swift, who, in fact, amazingly went on to play seven seasons as an outside linebacker for the Miami Dolphins, before he went on to become a doctor. So, this is a what-if amalgam and extension from facts into fiction, and, with any luck, some metaphorical resonance. My wife and many of our friends do not care about or like—some even abhor— the game of football. And, rightly so, given its violence and now, proven statistics of mental and physical disabling. Instead, "Riot Act" might be read as a fable about the passions, immersions, and demands of the creative process and, too, the trauma when those gifts are diminished.

These explanations are not meant to over-inflate but hopefully will be received, like the stories themselves, as humble efforts to joyously connect and tell tales.

T R A G E D Y

O F

M O D E R N

M A N

I N

T H R E E

A C T S

. . . by G A R R Y   B R O W N

*   *   *   *

The Tragedy of Modern Man in Three Acts... by Garry Brown

And before I typed ACT I at the top of the page, there was this date:"...
October 23rd, 1966—Sunday."

Which means I was 17 years old, would be 18 in November.

This was the fall of my senior year at Darien High School, Darien,
Connecticut. I was in Mr. Adams' Advanced English Class. Christopher
Adams. Chris Adams. The "No-Neck Porcupine." I never called him this
though some did, and, it is what he looked like. A stocky man, always dressed
in a grey or dark suit, bow-tie.

(My English teacher, sophomore year, was also very dapper, a
Dartmouth grad, Mr. Hayes; he was our class advisor. One afternoon he said
to me in a sly, dry-humored aside, "You're really a Babbitt, aren't you?" I
thought it was an honorific until I went and found Sinclair Lewis's novel, and
came away hurt, upset. Oh. A bull-shitter. A hypocrite. A shiny bravado with
no heart or soul. I was only sixteen. But he'd seen me: I was class president; he
attended all our class meetings; he saw me carry on, charm the multitudes and
do my Boston accented JFK imitation, anything for a laugh.)

In contrast, Mr. Adams was scary. He had an arrogant, almost pompous
air, with always a furrowed, concentrated brow. His short-cropped grey hair, a
crew-cut, was prickly-looking, very much like a porcupine. He had little or no
neck, as it flowed into his lumpy-looking body. He had a dominant presence,
even a bit tyrannical: you did not mess with Chris Adams. He picked on
people. He called them names. He called them out. He pressed and nudged
and judged, very harshly at times. What sense of humor he had was shared
mostly with the writers he had us reading:

—Whitman ("Are you 'multitudes', Mr. Wheat?" This was John Wheat, quiet,
easygoing, suddenly become bug-eyed);

—Emerson ("You must feel quite 'transcendental', Miss West, living in the East as you do, yes?" This was Newly West, tall and oh so bright and heady);
—Thoreau ("Ah, Mr. Dasher, the pond life for you, or does your family have a swimming pool?" John Dasher, and, in fact, they did have a pool, a very nice one in their back yard);
—Emily Dickinson ("A 'Nobody,' Mr. Leonard? Not you. If you're the editor of Neirad (our school yearbook, Darien spelled backwards), you must be a 'Somebody'!" Dan, an introvert, eyebrows raised and on alert, as if wakened from a deep trance);
—and several of the Greek plays, too ("Who doesn't like a 'Chorus line', right? But, the Greek 'Chorus' had things to say not songs to sing with a kicking up of legs, or have I got this wrong, Miss Risque, or would you prefer I say 'Ris-quay'?" Poor, lovely Robin, with a name that made her life perhaps a bit 'risky' especially around a sometimes-needling Mr. Adams).

But, how did we get to his asking us in the middle of October, 1966, to write an essay with this theme: the tragedy of modern man?

And how did I come to write a three-act play?

And what was I doing in that class in the first place?

I was a "jock." I had been a three-year starter on our football team; I was co-captain with Bob Woods on our basketball team; I was the catcher on our baseball team until my best bud—John Durland, "The D Man"—persuaded me to quit baseball and join him on the track team that spring.

Yes, I was in the National Honor Society but only because I was a grind; I studied, did well on all those tests, turned in papers on time.

But I was no intellectual, like Newly West or Dan Leonard or David Keys or John Wheat—all of whom could write and speak well, and, could verbally joust and hold their own with the intellectual tyrannist, Mr. Christopher Adams.

Mr. Adams called me "Teddy Bear." Was I a teddy bear? And what did that mean exactly?

In class, I sat next to Newly, who, when she spoke to me, seemed always to be looking at my forehead. I've since met a number of people who cannot look you in the eye. I would joke with her, "Newly? Oh Newly! Down here!" I'd rise in my seat to try to find her eyes, "Newly! Come down here, please, and we can talk..." She'd ignore me, until suddenly Mr. Adams would enter the class, all our eyes quickly, fearfully on him.

Yet David Keys, with what seemed like marbles in his mouth, would wave his fingers in front of his face as if to orchestrate the extended and intricate words of his explanation regarding Thoreau's *Walden,* "You see, Mr. Adams, *Walden* is not just one man's quest for freedom from the mundane and fealty to the common, it is also, perhaps, his lyrical and buoyant quest to restore poetry and, one might even say, 'transcendence' to his life…"

Or, John Wheat, who would lift off from his notebook doodlings and, pencil in hand, with no sense of fear and complete pencil waving of the air, explain in detail, "… Whitman is trying not only fitfully but elegantly in a language that is so plain yet fulsome, to create the American melting pot… I think, in a very divided country, before the Civil War and well after, he was, in his very immersive, all-seeing way, trying to create a symphonic America…"

While I, looking away, in no way raising my hand, would suddenly be called on—Mr. Adams' smile become a smirk, as if to say, 'Oh yes, the Teddy Bear, this should be good,' "Mr. Brown? Teddy Bear? How does Miss Emily Dickinson strike you? Any thoughts?"

I'd hem and haw and somehow say a few acceptable words, "Well, Mr. Adams, what strikes me, um, I just really appreciate her brevity. The short lines, the few words. At times they are real puzzles but their mysteries remind me of Stephen Crane's short, cryptic poems, which I also like a lot…"

Here I must acknowledge a crisis of confidence that was easing up but had begun a year before: my sophomore year I was in Mr. Hayes' English class, which went well. So well, that by my junior year I had joined Mr. Adams' Advanced English class. I was flattered and excited, until I began to feel my limits of expression. That is, with Mr. Adams' name-calling and intense questions, demands, I became hesitant, grappling over and over with doubts, my head stewing and second-guessing, so that any attempt to speak was inhibited.

That summer of my junior year, I could not speak: I suffered this enormous short-circuitry, red-faced and shamefully self-conscious. John, the D Man, tried to help me. Together, we would cruise the diners and donut shops or late afternoon beaches, playing frisbee and trying to meet girls. John, who was usually shy and I, who was the "hail fellow, well met," reversed roles: John would lead and I'd try to join in, say Hi, feebly uttering a few words, in hopes I could speak again.

Returning to Mr. Adams' Advanced English my senior year, thanks to John and our summer excursions, my confidence had begun to return. But, that week of our essay assignment, I began to feel overwhelmed as well as, strangely and even wonderfully, some indeterminate form of rebellion. I did not want a lot of words. I did not think I had a lot of words. Also, I didn't have a lot of time to write an elaborate ESSAY. I had football practice and a game to prepare for and oh, by the way, other classes. So, in the spirit of Emily Dickinson and Stephen Crane, I wanted to keep things brief, essential.

This is what I wrote:

... October 23rd, 1966—Sunday

— ACT I —

CHORUS
    Centuries have rolled away.
    Where there was Zeus and his gods
    There is God and Modern Man;
    Where there was Aristotle
    There are men of science;
    Where there was Aristotle
    There are men of politics
    Where there was Aristotle
    There are men of the arts;
    Where there were "answers"
    There are more questions.

    (Enter Modern Man dressed as John F. Kennedy)

MODERN MAN
    Where am I?
    What kind of fool am I?
    Who can I turn to?
    Who is my keeper?

CHORUS
> You are young and strong,
> A man among men.
> You are loved and yet hated.
> Look to God
> For when you die,
> Man must.

MODERN MAN
> I will not die
> For God is my Shepherd
> I shall not want
> He maketh me to lie down in green...
> > (Modern Man dead on a street in Dallas, Texas)

CHORUS
> Life will go on,
> Sorrow draws it out.
> As man questions God,
> Why?
> And with a mail-order rifle?

— ACT II —

CHORUS
> A hundred years
> He has been "free"
> Like the monkey in the zoo.

> (Enter Modern Man dressed as a Southern Black man, in a cotton shirt and brown pants)

MODERN MAN
> I ask no questions;
> I'm smart.
> I know my place
> I am anti-white

As my skin says
And I need no help
From them.
The Lord knows...
I mean well.

CHORUS
You used to say
"Yes, sir" and "Thank you, sir."

MODERN MAN
Yes, I used to.
But they got mean and nasty,
When we became even.
It got worse.

CHORUS
Today, life is better.
Now they listen
To what you yell.

MODERN MAN
Yes, they listen
But with closed ears.
And when they talk,
They speak to our skin
And never to us.

CHORUS
Well, it's not your soul
They kill?

MODERN MAN (As he is attacked by police dogs and police men watch)
Nope, it's the color of it.

— ACT III —

CHORUS (Looking at Modern Man dressed as an American soldier in
Vietnam, crouched behind foliage)
    He is camouflaged
    To look like a man,
    But he is young.
    He cannot vote
    But he carries a rifle.
    He plays a game
    Like football
    But for keeps.

    (To Modern Man) Do you not wonder?

MODERN MAN
    Wonder what?

CHORUS
    Why you are here?

MODERN MAN
    Yes, often.
    But I know.
    I must know...
    For my country...
    'Cause God willed it.
    Yes, that's it—God willed it.

CHORUS
    Are you sure?

MODERN MAN
    Yes, but...
    Well, no—
    Who are you anyway?

CHORUS
>No, you're not sure.
>Nobody is sure.
>And when you die
>Others will come and wonder
>And question and—

MODERN MAN
>What makes you
>Think I'll die?
>I'm young and healthy
>My girl's waiting
>Back home.
>I love her...
>And my family.
>If only I'd graduated.
>I would have,
>Except for that teacher
>She hated my guts—oh!
>(Modern Man slumps over, fatally wounded.)

I re-read this fifty-six years later. I live now on the West Coast, in a coastal town, much more diverse than a very WASPy and coastal Darien, Connecticut. I was going through boxes in the garage when I came across the xeroxed copy of my play. Quite surprisingly, a week or so later, an old high school chum (we were in a jug band together) sent me his copy of the play which I'd given him: "For the archive?" his note asked. 'For the archive,' as in something from long ago, and then, I look around, at our current world and country, and think, alas, it continues, 'the tragedy of modern man.'

In 1966, when I wrote this, our Political Science teacher, Jerry Wilhelm, one morning did not show up at Darien High. Eventually we were told he had committed suicide. The 60's were turbulent, nationally as well as locally, and I was a young man trying to figure out my place in it. For Jerry Wilhelm's class I wrote a paper called "Why Vietnam?" which my father read, shook his head, and muttered about. I was clearly wondering why America was there in the first place. My father, a Republican, wanted Nixon for his president; but I think, he, like a lot of us, was also impressed with this young Boston-accented JFK, kindred to my father's ilk, since my dad's dad, a grandfather we never knew — he died when my father was 20 — was one of the first doctors to have an X-Ray machine in the Boston area. JFK, with his New England sense of humor and intelligence, became acceptable in our family. My junior year I'd been part of this exchange program through the high school: I left our lily-white Darien community to spend a weekend with a Black fellow high-schooler, Willy, and his family in the Washington Heights section of New York City. The following weekend, Willy, came to our home in Darien. I was outgoing, Willy was less so, but we both loved sports and so we got along.

Clearly, all these aspects of our Darien in the 60's, our country in turmoil, fed into my considering 'modern man's tragedy' or tragedies. I don't have a clear image of how the play got written. I know I wrote it in my three-hole notebook first, loving the format of characters and speeches, just dialogue, and not a lot of exposition. Did I spend the week writing it? My sense is that it came in one fell swoop. I do know I typed it on my Olivetti Tippa portable typewriter, which I'd been using since 6th grade, when I first learned to type, given to me by my parents as a birthday gift.

I must have typed it up that Sunday, October 23, 1966, after Saturday's football game against Greenwich. I played hard but we lost, a close one, and the rest of the weekend into the week, I was carrying a load of shame, trying very hard to stay upbeat.

It was a week later when I saw Chris Adams coming my way. I made a beeline for the restroom, to stay clear of him.

"Mr. Brown? Garry!"

Oh shit. Why wasn't he calling, "Hey, Teddy Bear"? I stopped, turned around and met him half way.

"Mr. Adams. Yes, sir?"

"*The Tragedy of Modern Man,* yes?"

"Yes, sir. That theme. I gave it to you last Monday."

"You wrote a play, a play called *The Tragedy of Modern Man in Three Acts...*"

"Yes, sir."

"You wrote that?"

"Yes, sir."

"No, I mean, you sat down and wrote a play on that theme and called it—."

"*The Tragedy of Modern Man in Three Acts.* Yes, sir."

"You wrote that all by yourself?"

"Well. Um. Yes, sir, I wrote that. All by myself."

"It's brilliant... You're sure you wrote it?"

"Yes, sir."

"I'm going to make sure it's part of the upcoming Literary Magazine. It's quite something. Well done, Brown."

"Thank you, Mr. Adams. Wow. Thank you."

"Okay then."

He kept staring at me.

I kept waiting for him to be finished, a cue to leave.

He started to turn and then, "You really wrote that?"

I nodded, sheepishly smiled, "Yes, sir. I really did write it."

"This is very exciting."

He turned and began to leave.

I didn't know what to think.

About ten paces down the hall, he turned and said, almost angrily, "You still owe me that essay!"

As far as I can remember, Mr. Adams never again called me "Teddy Bear." It was always just "Brown" or "Mr. Brown" or even now and then, simply, "Garry."

Six years later, the spring into summer of 1972, I was already a year out of college. I had spent the summer of 1971 in Tennessee and then that fall, had backpacked through Europe with my then college sweetheart. We broke up, I was back home in Darien, writing poems and stories and not sure who I was and where I was headed. I was working by day in a nursing home, drawing pen and inks, pretty sure I was going to be a painter until in the late spring I took a community theatre acting class.

Working on the poems, I thought of Mr. Adams. I looked up his address in the phone book and jotted down his phone number. A week later, after I had typed up about twenty poems, I finally dredged up the courage and phoned him.

"Mr. Adams?"

"Yes. Who is this?"

"Not sure you'll remember me but I was in your advanced English. It's Garry Brown."

"Of course. 'The Tragedy of Modern Man In 3 Acts'."

"Why yes."

"Amherst, right?"

"Yes-sir... I graduated last year, and well, I have these poems I've been working on and wondered if I might drop them off, if you might read them."

"Of course. Can you come by this afternoon after 4pm?"

"Great. Thank you."

"Fine. See you then."

His house was a two-story grey shingled Cape Cod, with about 10 concrete steps up to the white front door. When Mr. Adams opened the door, I was so surprised: I still pictured him from my high school days, the grey or dark suits, the bow-tie, but here he was in a very preppy crisp dress-white shirt, tucked into a broad pair of navy Bermuda shorts! He did not invite me in, we made no small talk. We shook hands, he seemed glad to see me but still had a very intent, preoccupied air and made it very clear, "Garry, why don't you come by a week from today and I'll have these poems ready to return to you?" Surprised and pleased, I thanked him.

A week later, when I went to pick them up, I suspect I was hoping for praise. Perhaps he might become my writing mentor, or, at least, offer me some sense of direction, counsel, wisdom. All he said was this:

"Keep writing, Brown. Keep reading, lots of reading, and keep writing."

My *New Yorker* Cover

I was still living at home in Darien, Connecticut, in the summer of 1972. I'd returned from four months of back packing through Europe and had gotten a job as an orderly at Courtland Gardens nursing home in nearby Stamford. Cleaning bedpans by day, I was taking an acting class in the evening with Morris Carnovsky and his wife, Phoebe Brand.

To relax, I'd visit bookshops in Darien and nearby New Canaan and the one thrift shop in Darien—the bookshops to browse and see what was current, the thrift shop if I was going to actually buy a book. And Miss Burch's Burch Books, at the corner of the Post Road and the Darien railroad station, if, on those rare occasions, I was going to do both.

I was a man on a mission but I wasn't quite sure what that mission was: leaving college, I was pretty sure I wanted to become a painter, an artist. Once home from Europe, the love of writing—poems, stories, personal essays—had begun to kick in. Then, with my evenings free, I saw in the local paper, The Stamford Advocate, an ad for this acting class. So, I began investigating acting: I worked on a monologue from *Hamlet* with the Carnovskys as they helped inaugurate this new community theatre in Stamford called The Sterling Barn Theater.

I first saw Mandi at the New Canaan Bookshop, on Main Street, maybe a 10-minute walk from the New Canaan train station. The bookshop was posh, full of well-dressed ladies, sales clerks ready to help, and even better dressed ladies, housewives of the businessmen commuters, who were more than ready to buy. Then there was Mandi and I. Both of us a bit out of place in that exalted setting: she with her loose fitting, slightly risqué attire, straps and loops and open spaces near her thin arms and along her bony back; and me, in my loose khakis, sneakers, t-shirt, curly mussed-up brown hair and glasses, with a sketchbook under my arm, notepad in my back pocket.

Neither of us was buying that day; we were both just browsing. Books, at first, then one another. New Canaan was touted, among all of us who had grown up in neighboring Darien, these exalted Fairfield County high-priced "bedrooms of New York," as having the prettiest girls around. And Mandi was lovely—lithe, blonde, a very delicate kind of beauty. But she was thin, very thin, which for me, was a deal-breaker. So, as I approached the Art Book section and stared at that very finely shaped, almost porcelain face, with its sweet come-hither smile, I also realized how thin she was. I wasn't sure there was really enough there, for me—tall, over two hundred pounds, a mop-headed bumbler—to enjoy.

She must have thought differently. In the dense midst of the art books, she was muttering to herself, something about Bonnard, Pissarro, and Monet, when she turned to me, "Crazy, right?"

"I beg your pardon?"

"So polite! Look. They have Bonnard. They have Pissarro, see? But no Monet. How can that be?"

I now joined her, as we scanned the shelves, tennis-match style, going from the B's to the P's and back to the M's. Sure enough, not one book on Monet.

"Huh."

"More than 'huh'—more like 'horrible'!" The 'horrible' pronounced with a fake French accent: "whore—reeb—bluh!"

Of course, having just been in France, hoping to impress, I French-ishly, replied, "Bien sur!"

She laughed. I laughed. Ice broken.

That spring afternoon, we left the bookstore and headed down the block to have a coffee, or more likely back then, a malted or a soda. We started to when Mandi realized, "Oh dear, I just remembered, I have to be somewhere. I'm sorry."

"Okay, it's okay."

"But I'd really like to chat. Another time?"

"Of course. Great. When?"

"Um... how about..."

Mandi was an original, with a spritely effervescent energy; she was a very lithe, limber, and seductive Diana, independent in some ways, somewhat needy in others. We did meet, off and on, that spring into summer, in bookshops, coffeeshops, out and about.

She was an Art History buff and an artist; I never saw any of her artwork. I was keeping a journal, writing poems and short stories. I also continued to do a series of pen and inks, town and country scenes as well as a series of portraits from the nursing home, the elders, along with some of the orderlies and nurses.

How it came up, I'm not sure. I had always loved *The New Yorker*, grew up on its cartoons and covers and harbored this distant fantasy, a lark, a joke, ha, what if I could one day do a *New Yorker* cover? I never mentioned this to anyone, never pursued it, not seriously, until the afternoon Mandi met me at the Baskin Robbins on the Post Road in Darien.

I had just finished my 6am to 3pm shift at Courtland Gardens. I had my sketchbook with me. Mandi noticed it and asked if she could look.

"Sure."

"You always have a sketchbook with you, don't you? Since that first day we met…"

She began turning pages. Rather than turning the pages quickly, mindlessly, Mandi was really looking.

"These are very good. Oh dear."

"Thanks. What?"

"I think I know that man. Is he a judge?"

"In fact, he is. You know him? A friend of the family?"

"My father's friend."

"Your dad's a lawyer or, a judge?"

"No. Dad's a cartoonist. A very good one."

"Really? That's kind of cool."

"It is. And so are these. Really. Garrett, you have real talent."

"Thanks, Mandi."

"This nursing home series is special but—like this one—were you on the train when you did this?"

"Yeah. A late afternoon, coming back from the city, a whole bunch of commuters and this wonderful bald pate, looming."

"This would make a great *New Yorker* cover, it's very real and very funny, too, in its way."

"Really?"

"Really."

"Huh."

"Not 'huh' but—vraiment!" Again, the French accent, and again my lame reply:

"Merci beaucoup!"

"Your French is actually pretty good, your accent. "

"Merci encore! Again. Thanks!"

We laughed, sipped our ice cream shakes. She continued paging through my sketchbook until she suggested I meet her dad.

"But, why? Isn't he a cartoonist?"

"For *The New Yorker*. "

"Oh. Man, I love *The New Yorker*."

"Me, too. Kind of. They own my dad."

"But, Mandi, these aren't cartoons. "

"I know. But this one, I'm telling you, it'd make a great cover. With no color, just the black lines on white. You have a really wonderful line, kind of Matisse mixed with Jules Feiffer."

"Wow, I love them both. Thank you!"

"I want my dad to see these. With any luck, he'd put in a good word with Lee Lorenz, the Art Editor at *The New Yorker* and hey, you never know, right?"

"Right."

Funny, I was excited and not. I had learned to draw from Superman and Archie comics. I had loved cartoons, once upon a time. Then, in college, I was mentored by the renowned American painter, Fairfield Porter. The jury was still out concerning my artistic ambitions since I was now intrigued with this acting class and had a growing love for writing. I wanted to be a serious artist, not a cartoonist. And yet. *The New Yorker*. A cover for *The New Yorker*. That would be something. Though, really? Didn't I have bigger fish to fry? I was very adamant about becoming a Serious Artist.

But... Charles Saxon.

Mandi had told me her last name but it had never registered. Now it did. I got nervous. My God. "SaXon," those cartoons, satirical, often biting, sometimes heartwarmingly funny. That exaggerated X of his name, the way he signed it, with a real flourish. My God.

Charles SaXon. *The New Yorker*. Really?

Here's where memory and fiction begin to do battle: I have this vague recollection that, on an evening in early August, Mandi brought me to her parents distinguished looking two-story home, with its expansive and very green front lawn; we passed through a heavy and slow-moving white front door into a living room with a grand bay window where her parents sat. Mandi's mother rose cheerily and bustled, her father sat almost wearily and hardly budged. Introductions were made. I handed Mr. Saxon my drawings.

Rather than my sketchbooks, Mandi had suggested I buy a black portfolio. With her help, we had ripped out drawings, all pen and inks, about twenty, and put them in an ascending order, in terms of a gradual seduction of her dad's eye, in the impressive black leather holder.

I stood there, like a fool, as if I expected him to open the black leather sleeves and have a look. He placed the portfolio on the floor beside him and watched Mandi, his wife, and me kind of gadfly about him. Actually, I just stood there, slow and dumb, while the two women did a lovely and charitable Q and A.

Mandi: Garrett lives in Darien.

Mrs. Saxon: How nice.

Mandi: He went to Amherst, graduated last year.

Mrs. Saxon: Good for you—Garrett, is it?

Me: Yes. With two r's and two t's.

Mrs. Saxon: Of course. Would you like something to drink, Garrett, with two r's and two t's?

We all laughed except for Mr. Saxon. He continued to slowly sip his drink, look out the bay window and now and then give me an impartial once-over.

Me: No thanks. I just wanted to say Hi.

Mandi: Dad, you must look at Garrett's pen and inks. They're very good. One for sure but maybe a couple others would make great *New Yorker* covers.

Mr. Saxon: he nods, raises his glass as if to toast.

Me: Thanks, Mr. Saxon, for your interest.

Mr. Saxon: he raises his glass again, another toast.

Mandi: Please, Daddy, look at them and then put in a good word with your buddy Lorenz.

Mr. Saxon: Ah, Sir Lee Lorenz. Of course! Again, the raised glass, the feigned toast.

Me: Well. It's a beautiful evening. I didn't mean to interrupt.

I start to go.

Mrs. Saxon: Oh no, you mustn't leave. Please stay, join us for dinner!

Mandi: Yes, Garrett, why don't you?

Me: Thanks. I'd better not. Great to meet you and thanks, Mandi, I'll see you around, okay?

I hope this isn't what actually happened. It reminds me too much of growing up in the 50's in those vaunted suburban towns of Connecticut, the drinking, the false cheer masking the downright sadness, or what was it?

Towards the end of August, I met Mike Wolcott, a lawyer for IBM who lived at 55th Street and Lexington. He needed a roommate: he was paralyzed from the waist up. He'd contracted polio during the 50's epidemic. He couldn't use his arms and needed a roommate to help him eat his evening meal as well as help him when he stayed in the city on the weekends. This in exchange for my room and board. Just as I was about to move into the Big City, I heard from Mandi. Her father liked my drawings, he'd contacted Lee Lorenz, I was to phone there and set up an appointment. She gave me the phone and the address of *The New Yorker*.

I was incredulous. I had been packing, upstairs in my attic bedroom. My mother had called to me, that I had a phone call, then rejoined my dad on the porch. It was dusk. They were having cocktails. I stood in my mother's pink kitchen and just about collapsed as Mandi delivered this news.

"Really?"

"Really! Vraiment!"

"Okay."

"Just 'okay'?"

"No, I mean, Mandi, this is incredible. Thank you!"

"Don't thank me just, isn't this *great?* My dad's such a—well, he can be harsh but, I even checked with him twice, to make sure he wasn't teasing. He really likes your work and thinks Lee will, too!"

"I—I'm speechless. I mean, really, thank you so much!"

"You're welcome. So, call *The New Yorker* and, you know—good luck!"

A few days later, after the move, and sitting in Mike's living room that looked out from the third floor onto a rooftop of generators and a horizon of other rooftops as well as the walls of taller buildings, I phoned. I was told to drop off my portfolio—the receptionist used that word "portfolio"—and said the best day would be a Monday, late morning; she told me which floor, and that I should make sure "Attention: Lee Lorenz" was on the portfolio along with my address and phone.

On a Monday, in November, 1972, I visited *The New Yorker* offices on the north side of 43rd Street between Fifth and Sixth Avenues. The building was not far from the Algonquin Hotel, which got me thinking about writers and humorists (and *The New Yorker* cartoonist/writer, James Thurber) who once gathered there. I was surprised: the *New Yorker* building was run-down and musty. It felt like an old high school, the lighting dim, the linoleum floors worn. I found the receptionist on the third floor.

"Hi, I'm Garrett Brown."

"Hello, I'm Lois. How can I help you?"

"Was it you I spoke with about dropping off my portfolio, my drawings, for Mr. Lorenz to look at?"

"Might have been. You can just place it right here."

Lois was an attractive woman, perhaps in her 40's, a full head of brownish hair, a pencil in her right ear, glasses, and a typewriter in front of her, pens, and a black phone off to her right.

She patted the open space to her left, an expansive area of dark wood desktop.

"Okay..." I did this. "That's it?"

"That's it. I'll make sure he gets it."

"Great. Okay... You don't want me to just take it and give it to him in person?"

"Not necessary. He'll swing by eventually and pick it up. You did put your return address and phone on it, yes?"

"I did, yes."

"Then you're all set."

"Okay then. Thanks."

"Sure."

I started to leave, then hesitated, "Excuse me, Lois, but are you a writer?"

"Me? Ha! Oh no, I just help with letters that need writing, follow-up stuff. Mostly I guess I'm what you'd call a 'gatekeeper'."

"Right. And a very good one, too!"

"You're sweet. Now do not worry, I'll take good care of your drawings. He'll get them."

"Thanks. I guess I am a little nervous."

"No need. They're in good hands, you'll see."

My first weeks in "the city that never sleeps" were strange and wonderful: I had my mornings and afternoons free and then had to be back at Apt 3C by

5:30pm. Norma, from the Caribbean, was in the 'ship's kitchen' fixing dinner which I would eat with and feed to Mike.

Though my room and board were solved, I still needed to be making some money so I went to an employment agency where I billed myself as a housepainter, got one job. Then, two weeks later, I became a messenger, a great way to walk the streets, ride the subway, and get to know the city.

I wrote in my journal, took long strolls, visited all sorts of bookshops and thrift shops, and watched people like crazy. Was I going to be a writer or a painter and what about the mysteries of acting? Or, was I going to be a *New Yorker* cartoonist? Again, I had no compelling ambitions—I was so enthralled with the city and all these possibilities. I would visit coffeeshops and do pen and inks. I wrote poems and attempts at short stories. Just down the block, at St Peter's Episcopal Church, there was "Theatre at Noon," these very short plays with wonderful, funny actors. I went and was so thrilled and impressed. Again, the acting impulses rose up and called. Until there was another call.

Almost a month after I dropped off my portfolio, a woman phoned:

"Hello. I'm calling from *The New Yorker*. Is this Garrett... ?"

"Yes. Is this Lois?"

"Oh no, I work with Mr. Lorenz. My name's Barb'."

"Hi, Barb'."

"Hi, and is this Garrett M. Brown?"

"Yes, with two r's and two t's."

"Of course. I see that right here on your portfolio. So..."

"Am I going to be a *New Yorker* cartoonist, Barb?"

"Ha. Maybe. One day. Mr. Lorenz wanted me to call and let you know that you can come retrieve your drawings."

"Oh. Okay. How soon?"

"Any time. We're pretty much open from 9am to 5pm, Monday to Friday, unless you have a differently scheduled appointment. Okay?"

"Okay. Thanks, Barb'."

"You're welcome, Mr. Brown. Have a good day."

After my messenger work, the next afternoon, I swung by *The New Yorker* building, trapsed the dingy linoleum halls. A thin man with thick black glasses was at Lois's desk, on the phone. When he saw me, he quizzically pointed to my portfolio, I nodded, he continued listening, now and then saying into the phone, "I see," and "Sure." I picked up my portfolio and departed.

I never saw Sir Lee Lorenz, never heard from him, and there was no note attached to my portfolio. Or was there? If there was, it went something like this:

"Dear Mr. Brown, thank you for letting us consider your work.
Please continue to keep us in mind and one day, who knows? You are quite gifted and if it were up to Charles Saxon or his daughter, Mandi, you'd already be on staff. But, as this is all pure fantasy and conjecture, just know, you will always have a friend at *The New Yorker*. Sincerely, Lee Lorenz."

Riot Act

1.

He sat on the padded table waiting for Tony, the training room dimly lit. Eyed his white bandaged fingers, not unlike a boxer's—his knuckles, dried, rough, some creases of blood.

Tony would warm him up, some heat, a massage.

He felt heavy, slow—he *was* heavy. He didn't want to move, let alone move other bodies.

And the joy?

A kid, a teen, a college athlete—now a pro—how did this happen?

It's just a game but… he raises his head, watches through the training room windows.

But where is everybody? Jake, Dallas, the Mags, the Cooze, Jerry, Butch, Coach Del… ?

There's an enormous amount of love here, among these men.

2.

Ever since his brother pulled him outdoors, onto the front lawn, gave him the football—

Come on, run at me, he said. Run.

He looked at the taut reddish ball, its speckled leather, felt its grainy bulk in his hands. Then, as he'd seen—he was ten years old—cradled it in his right arm and ran.

That's it, run hard!

He did. He didn't go left or right or try to run away. He didn't giggle or joke, pretend to run and then disappear behind the house. No. He ran right at his brother, who bumped him, shoved him. He fell. He ran again—right at him—hard!

The solid scrunch—the jar—the thrump!

His body smothered.

He loved it.

3.

His brother still loved the game.

His father, too, dead now.

His kid brother, not so much, even though he was the one who brought Mom to the games.

And Julie, too, his girlfriend, or wait—Jesus, isn't she my wife now?

Oh God! Tickets!

Did I reserve their tickets? Jesus.

'The Big Game.'

But every game was big, was a mountain, a steeple chase, a multitude of sins.

Worlds within worlds.

He tried to raise his thick, solid arms.

He couldn't. And his neck now, a sudden knifing, the pain pierced, then slowed, throbbed.

Jesus, I gotta get ready. Where's Tony?

He closed his eyes, tried to slow his breath, tried to pray.

4.

His brother, a tight end, All State Connecticut, Little All American in college, invited to try out with the Chicago Bears. He didn't go. Why?

Still an unsolved mystery.

Himself, 6'5", almost two-twenty when he played freshman football, a small college in the Northeast. But the coach was a screamer, killed his joy for the game. So, it was basketball the rest of his college years.

Senior year, a letter: Gil Brandt, Dallas Cowboys football scout, wanted to know his statistics, time in the 40, "We've had success with basketball players becoming defensive backs…" Invited to try out.

Flattered and curious, he showed up in Texas, ran a good 40, made some strong, athletic plays. A year later, 20 pounds heavier, he became one of their youngest outside linebackers.

He was funny and he hit like a ton of bricks. They called him 'Riot Act,' and then, just 'Riot.'

He watched film, he listened, he grew up. Learned that emotion (rage) was not enough. Had to become wily, too, that competitive edge.

5.

Head bowed still, he smiled, watched his swollen bandaged fingers.

Where? Where does it come from, this desire?

That sober even sullen 'game face,' yes. He remembered his mother's refrain, *I don't like it. I don't know you. Some Cro-Magnon man, some prehistoric creature. Who are you?*

He laughed, raised his head to the overhead neon lights, his face and body a pale reflection in the training room windows. He heard it: a maniacal laugh.

How his whole body, demeanor could shift, transform. 'An extra gear,' some said, but he only felt this rush, this toe to gut thrill of energies, not rage but rages, a kind of seeing red but tempered.

That first hit.

That's all.

Nerves, distemper, even doubts until Boom! Pop! Crunch!

A cartoon of sounds until the shaken earth becomes his soul.

He is an unbridled muscular fluency.

6.

When he's off the field, quiet, slow, alone like now, he does wonder. He does doubt.

How much longer? Will his body let him? *Will his body tell him?*

No longer a kid, he's a thirty-one-year-old man.

The money, yes, the parties, too: crazy off-season nights, when locals are proud, buy you drinks, buy you dinner, and old friends from high school, a few from college.

But none of that is real. It doesn't register, not deep down.

Superficial glories.

Because this, this is it.

This is felt and full and real.

No crisis of the soul on the field, in play. The flow, the incessant flow of the game. The blood flow, the adrenalin flow, the life flow, yes:

This is where I live, on that field, in that arena.

7.

He thinks of the other players through the years, the good guys, the jerks.

Magnum in high school, a Rah-Rah, co-captain, loud, angry. *How good was he, really?*

Irony: Magnum played linebacker in high school, then at a small college, and then? Their ten-year reunion, a businessman, smug, arrogant. No words between them.

Maybe he hates the sport now, thinks it's too violent, too dangerous.

Or, Jack, a small tight end in high school, ushered him through his first Hell Week when he, Riot (then known as Dougie), made the team, the only sophomore to start.

Jack saw. Jack knew, stayed in touch, after high school, even showed up at one of his college basketball games: 'You love hoops,' he said, 'but you wait. Football's not over, you wait.' *How'd he know?*

We know. Just as I know when I see the rookies. Impressions. Moves, on and off the field.

The way 'the Kid' catches balls and winks, that cocksureness on the field, his sweet low-key 'Yes-sir' off.

He's good. *He'll make it. Won't he?*

8.

Making it. Doing it. Toughing it out.

This question of being a man. A stand-up guy. Be a man. Stand your ground.

No, it's more than that, much more.

Likened to war, soldiers, 'he's a warrior;' or animals, 'he's an animal,' 'a beast.'

But that's not it.

I'm a grown man playing a kid's game.

I'm a professional. *I show up. I'm here.*

I'm ready. I'm prepared but—

The gift is in the sport, the art, the craft. Yes, we slam and shove and ram, dig in. Yes, we grunt and scream and cuss and spit.

Look deeper: the shimmy, the shake and bake, the lateral, the spiral, the fine touch, the soft hands—*penetrate beyond, within:*

The violence is the circus barker, the easy draw, the façade. *Go further.* Smell the grass, the dirt, the sweat—*observe the flight of angels.*

9.

I am not just an athlete, a warrior, a beast. *Look further.*

And yes, who am I talking to?

Tony, dammit! Where's Tony? My goddamned back hurts, my eyes keep welling up, blurry. My neck, Jesus. On game day?

I'm a man, too.

First a human being who loves this wild sport, this transcendence, this rigorous preparation for flight, fluency, the intricacies of all these maneuvers—offense, defense, special teams.

It is a livid map, this whole array of strategies and maneuvers, of a very complicated world.

I'm a part of this, small cog/big wheel, and, yes, okay, every day I have something to prove, *and when I don't, then it's time. Then, I'll stop.*

10.

Muscle memory and then the mind, thoughts: *No thinking!* My first real coach would shout.

Johnny—Coach John Marr.

A psychologist, an Irish shaman.

He got inside, he saw you, he penetrated:

Your shoelace is untied!

What?

Your shoelace!

I'd look down. Wham!

The football flew at me.

Don't ever look down or away. No! *Eyes on the ball!*

A twinkly-eyed man who studied our character, who watched us, who listened, who measured and tested, how he prepared us.

Such care, such belief, such love, really. Rare now, and I'm still hungry for it.

Muscle and no-mind. Unceasing preparation for the day, game day... *of no-mind, no hesitation.*

Just this ache and muster and thrust. This steady drumbeat, pulse of unbridled joy.

Yes: no time but this expansive, abrasive present.

11.

His coaches, yes, those who believed in him: Maute, Mehr, Wilson, John Marr, of course, and the Darp.

He told the Darp, No more college football. His studies, he explained, and one sport: hoops. He never told Darp about freshman football, the grad student assistant coach, a screamer.

True, Riot wasn't a star athlete, a natural, no. He was a mime, an imitator, still finding his legs, his balance, his way.

Until Coach Wayne, the grad assistant coach, slammed his helmet, shouted, pointed, that open mouth of venom. No humor, no backing off, no reprieve.

It ripped his heart apart, nightmares, panic, confusion, tears.

No. This was not fun. I do not like this man. Play for him? Why?

After the game in Hartford, a loss, sitting by his locker, his best friend found him, touched his damp shoulder pad, Hey, buddy...

He looked up, then down, then leaned into his knees and sobbed.

12.

Like he was doing now. Head bowed. Neck on fire. Eyes ablaze. These small pebbles, globules, round and marbly until they ran down his cheeks, dripped off, down onto his knees.

His eyes still shut.

No mind... just clouds, fuzziness, and then roused, as if fired up, eyes open:

Jesus! Tears? I'm crying? What the—

Tony rushes in, "Riot! Sorry, son. Sorry you had to wait."

Tony, olive complexion, Italian, balding, grey hairs along the sides, a toothpick always in his mouth (how he quit smoking and it stayed).

"Okay, Riot. You okay? You're all wet. I'll get a towel. Just a sec'."

Riot holds onto the padded table, legs swing a bit, his body white, stolid, stonelike.

"Here, Riot. Here's a towel. Oh, here's the Doc', too."

13.

The doctor?

Doc' McGarry, team doctor, soft spoken. A weariness, a quiet that penetrates, observes, a gentle touch.

"Hey, Riot son, raise your head? Thanks."

A pencil-thin flashlight, white beams, into both eyes.

"That's it, follow my finger."

He does.

"Good. Sorry for the wait."

Tony standing by. Tony watching, tooth-pick shifting, left, right, right, left.

"Christ, what an f-ing game, huh, Doc?"

Riot watches both men.

"What's going on, Doc'? I gotta get ready, suit up. It's getting late."

"You're fine right here, Riot," says the Doc.'

Touches his neck, shoulders.

"Ow! Jesus!"

Another spray of pain, scissors and knives slicing.

"Jesus, Doc,' what are you doing?"

"Big hit, Riot," says the Doc.

"Knocked the crap outa him," adds Tony. "For a big loss, too."

"Yes-sir," nods Doc,' "but that's it for today, Riot. That's it."

14.

"That's it? What are you talkin'? I gotta—."

    "Sit, Riot. Stay. What day is it?"

    "Um…"

    "Who's the President?"

    "Aw, Jesus, come on, guys, I gotta get ready."

    "Okay, Riot. Get dressed."

    "There we go."

    "Street clothes."

    "What?"

    "And, Tony…"

    Doc' pulls Tony over, hand on shoulder, words, quiet. Tony nods, Doc' leans further in.

    And then?

    Riot forgets. A drift of moments.

    Locker, clothes, shoes, ambulance, a hospital room, hospital lights, faces, bright faces, and sleep.

    And cramps and screams in the night, startled, awakened.

    "Who screamed?"

    "It's okay, son," says the older nurse. "You did."

15.

The second night he couldn't get back to sleep.

    They'd all been there… Doc McGarry, his mom, his two brothers, and Julie. He kept looking at her, staring, and she'd said, "What, honey?" He laughed, shook his head, and then he spotted the ring on her finger.

    Okay, okay, I'm not going crazy, we are married.

    One more night, the Doc said, just one more night.

    Jesus. I really don't like this.

    And then he slept. Until he didn't. *A scream, another scream. Jesus!*

    "You okay, Mr. Riot?"

    "Who are you? Where's the old woman?"

    "That's no old woman, that's my mom."

    "What?"

    "My mom was with you last night."

"She's your mom?"

"Yes-sir."

Riot says nothing, stares at the much too brightly lit doorway.

"That was some game, I mean, you mauled that guy. Think he broke some ribs..."

"Who?"

"That Detroit halfback, he got pretty banged up."

"Oh."

"You wanna see the video? It's all over YouTube."

"No. Oh Jesus..."

Riot got up and limped quickly to the john, just in time.

"Arrgghh! Aw shit..." He kept vomiting, over and over, "Christ... Arggghhh!"

"You need some help, sir?"

"No! Just shut the door and leave me alone."

"Yes-sir. I'll be just outside if you need me."

The door clicked close. Silence. But for Riot's dry heaves and sour breathing.

Christ, what is this?

16.

Back in bed, he just lay there, slow, exhausted.

The screams... Coach Wayne, screaming at Riot, making him feel small, dumb, not wanted. Finally, Riot was screaming back at Coach Wayne, at everything. Screaming and screaming. But, the pain, his head on fire, non-stop, the throbbing, the heavy downbeat of hitting and hitting and screaming and screaming... *Jesus, why won't it stop?*

The male nurse, James, stayed seated outside Riot's room, Number 301. He sat there, confused, upset. What could he do? This ballplayer was a real star, a stud. He loved watching him play. It wasn't the vomiting. It was the tears. This great athlete, this good man. James could hear him. It didn't stop for a long time. He just kept crying and—crying. And then, it stopped.

No, it can't be like this, it can't end this way, I love to play, I love this game... these guys, Oh God, please, what is this? I don't want this to ever end... PLEASE.

Repetitions

We Want to Acknowledge

This anthology is dedicated to the late Holly Prado Northup. Over the span of forty years, each of us studied with Holly in one or another of her ongoing writing workshops. We continue to be grateful for her critical guidance and constant support. Holly also played an important part in our personal lives: Marie and Garrett met in Holly's Tuesday night workshop in 1994 and married 15 years later. Barbara and Bill, married in 1989, were brought together by a personals ad in the New York Review of Books. They discovered during their first phone call that they had both been in Holly's writing workshops.

The late Glenna Morrison, our friend and virtual author's assistant, inspired this anthology. Her casual suggestion one day in 2020 led to this book. Beyond this acknowledgement, we offer our sincere thanks for the wide variety of work we have called on her to do through the years. In addition to designing the Lagoon House Press website, she also created Marie's and Barbara's websites; proofread Barbara's *When Water Was Everywhere* as well as Marie's *Daughter of the Enemy;* and she guided the publicity campaign for *When Water Was Everywhere.* Always generous, always wise in her advice—Lagoon House Press appreciates all that Glenna did for us.

Marie and Barbara thank their writing groups, led by the late Holly Prado Northup. Marie's poems and Barbara's short stories were written over a span of twenty-five years. Many writing group participants deserve credit for their help. We thank you all. For brevity, we will name those who accompanied our writing journeys since Holly's retirement in 2017. Thus, our thanks to Maria Brahme, Toni Fuhrman, Joan Isaacson, Kathy Lazarus, Marlene Saile, Carine Topal, and Cecilia Woloch, and—when we began to hold our monthly meetings on Zoom due to the pandemic—to Dr. Jill Singer in London and Pamela Shandel in Paris.

Marie and Garrett are indebted to Cecilia Woloch, as an editor of both poetry and prose, for bringing the high polish to their writing. Marie adds Dr. Jill Singer for her close reading of Marie's introductions to her poetry collections and Terry Andrews for his meticulous proofreading. Garrett thanks EST-LA (Ensemble Studio Theatre-Los Angeles) for debuting the three short stories in this anthology, two on Zoom and one, pre-pandemic, in the theatre. Barbara thanks Dinah Berland for her prompt editorial assistance. She is grateful to her grandson, Kai Goldfein, for his pen and ink sketch of the diving camp for the story "The Raft of Medusa."

Bill Davis credits his interest in photography to his service in the U.S. Army from 1964 to1967. While stationed in Japan, Bill and three of his Army buddies went out and bought 35mm cameras. That began his lifelong practice and love of photography.

We thank, posthumously, attorney Paul Crane for his assistance in setting up Lagoon House Press as a legal entity.

Ellison / Goodreau's Mike Ellison designed *Three Writers / One Photographer*. We thank him for enduring endless conversations and changes as Mike strove to accommodate each of our wishes and concerns.

In all our publications, Cahuenga Press remains a model of a longtime working relationship. We are grateful for their support.

Who We Are

During their car trips to Holly Prado's Tuesday morning writing workshop, a communal dreaming and brainstorming began among Barbara Crane, Marie Pal-Brown, and Kathy Lazarus.

With Kathy needing to travel and be with family, those discussions moved to the Long Beach living rooms and dining tables of Barbara and husband Bill Davis (the photographer), and Marie and husband Garrett M. Brown (the third writer).

Eventually, with Barbara energizing the legal details and format, Bill organizing the finances, Marie consulting with other small presses, and Garrett offering an array of logo designs, Lagoon House Press came into being in 2015.

Inspired by Cahuenga Press, a cooperative of Los Angeles poets, LHP chose to broaden that vision to include fiction, memoir, plays, photography as well as poetry.

In 2016, LHP debuted its first publication, Barbara Crane's award-winning historical novel, *When Water Was Everywhere;* that was followed by Marie Pal-Brown's elegiac memoir of growing up in post-war Germany, *Daughter of The Enemy* in 2018, and Toni Fuhrman's well received novel, *The Second Mrs. Price,* in 2019.

Three Writers / One Photographer is LHP's fourth publication.

In the spring/summer of 2024, LHP will publish its fifth work, Garrett M. Brown's hybrid memoir/novel, *Tin Sea.*

Garrett M. Brown is a film, television, and theatre actor who also writes and paints. He is a long-time member of Ensemble Studio Theatre in New York and EST LA in Los Angeles.

His plays, *Ambulance Men, Home by Dusk, The Foolish Angel,* and his solo works, *Book Of Comforts* and *What's Funny In A Dark Time?* were produced in Los Angeles; *Americana,* in NY City.

Candlelight Vigils, his one-minute videos begun during the pandemic, can be found on Facebook and Instagram.

His short play, *Good. Fine.* debuted in June 2022, as part of EST-LA's Early Bird Special festival of new work.

His poetry has appeared in the Valyermo Chronicle, and his memoir gone rogue, *Tin Sea,* will be published by Lagoon House Press.

Born in Battle Creek, Michigan, Garrett grew up in Connecticut, graduated from Amherst College, and lived in New York City for 20 years before moving to Los Angeles. He resides in Long Beach, California.

Barbara Crane is a novelist and short story writer. Her 2016 novel, *When Water Was Everywhere,* won the Beverly Hills Book Award for historical fiction. Her previous novel, *The Oldest Things in the World,* published in 2002, captured a Silver Medal in ForeWord Magazine's annual literary awards. She is currently at work on a third novel.

Barbara's short stories and personal essays have appeared in a variety of publications, including the *Los Angeles Times, Sun* magazine, the *Birmingham Arts Journal,* and *Open: Journal of Arts & Letters.* Her travels in Latin America, India, the Middle East, and Africa have often suggested themes or settings for her work.

In addition to fiction writing, Barbara has pursued careers, usually simultaneously, as a business journalist, instructor, and corporate communications consultant. She grew up in Los Angeles, graduated from UC Berkeley and has lived in Long Beach, California, for over 40 years.

Bill Davis is a photographer, writer, and editor. His photographs have been published in Long Beach newspapers and on various websites.

He is particularly enthralled with nature photography. Birds and whales of many varieties comprise a large part of his portfolio.

His travels in North America, Asia, Africa and western Europe have inspired many compelling human images as well.

His taste in reading is wide—from crime novels to David Foster Wallace. His favorites include Patrick O'Brian's Aubrey-Maturin novels and Hilary Mantell's *Wolf Hall*.

Bill is the only partner in Lagoon House Press who was born in Southern California. He grew up in the San Bernardino Mountains and the San Gabriel Valley. He graduated from California State University, Los Angeles, and has lived in Long Beach for 35 years.

Marie Pal-Brown was born and raised in a small town near Cologne, Germany. After she graduated from high school in 1957, she attended Durham University in England and took exams at Cambridge, then completed her B.A. and M.A. degrees at the SDI, the Applied Language Academy of the University of Munich.

In the early sixties, she emigrated to California, where she married her first husband, with whom she shares three children.

She is the co-author, together with Professor Wolf Friederich, of three works of lexicography. Her poetry and personal essays have appeared in various anthologies and literary magazines. *Daughter of the Enemy,* a memoir about her post-war years in Germany, was published by Lagoon House Press in 2018. It was a finalist in the Annual Beverly Hills Book Awards and has been incorporated into the curriculum of the German Department at Lawrence University in Appleton, WI.

Marie resides in Long Beach, California.

Printed in the USA
CPSIA information can be obtained
at www.ICGtesting.com
CBHW040330030424
6254CB00005B/9